A WARM BED ON A COLD NIGHT
AND OTHER STORIES

Every good wish

John B Keane

A WARM BED ON A COLD NIGHT

AND OTHER STORIES

JOHN B. KEANE

MERCIER PRESS

MERCIER PRESS
PO Box 5, 5 French Church Street, Cork
        and
16 Hume Street, Dublin

Trade enquiries to CMD DISTRIBUTION,
55a Spruce Avenue, Stillorgan Industrial Park, Blackrock, Dublin

© John B. Keane, 1997

ISBN 1 85635 184 X

10 9 8 7 6 5 4 3 2 1

A CIP record for this book is available from the British Library.

TO EILEEN AND TONY
FOR KEEPING ME STILL TO THE GOOD

Printed in Ireland by Colour Books Ltd.

CONTENTS

A Warm Bed on a Cold Night

MANY YEARS AGO, WHEN I was a garsún, I was friendly with an aged bachelor who had a unique method of heating his bed on a cold night. He did not require permanent heating, just something to start him off. He was opposed to artificial heating, as he called it, and would have no truck with hot water bottles or electric blankets.

He lived in the countryside, a mere stone's throw from the tar road, so that he was never short of callers. These varied from people who had lost their way to wandering tramps and outcast itinerants as well as journeymen, tradesmen and unapproved evangelists.

Anyway, when nights were frosty or when the snow blanketed the countryside, our friend would admit one of the aforementioned and provide him with shelter for the night. It was the custom in those distant days to allow a wanderer a place beside the fire until daybreak when he would be given a mug of tea, a few slices of bread and butter, and a boiled egg or two. Then he would be sent upon his way to prey upon somebody else.

Upon being informed by our bachelor friend that he would be granted shelter for the night, the wanderer would be profuse in his thanks, calling down all God's blessings in the most colourful fashion on his benefactor.

'Spare your thanks,' my elderly bachelor friend would inform him, 'but go up instead to my bedroom. Then strip to the pelt and proceed to warm my bed. Let that be your thanks. When the bed has been fully warmed, you may come downstairs and take your place on this settle bed beside the hearth.'

Willingly the wanderer would disrobe in the dark bedroom and stay in the cold bed until it was warmed. Sometimes a wearier wanderer than most would fall asleep and he would have to be forcibly removed. However, most did what was expected of them.

Our ancient friend would then disrobe and take his place in the warm hollow between the sheets. Sometimes the bed would be very warm and other times not so warm. It depended upon the age, size and health of the would-be warmer.

It was a good system, from which both sides benefited. He was, I must concede, a trifle choosy about the type of person he would allow into his bed.

If there was any sort of whiffiness off the candidate, he would not be dispatched upstairs to begin the bed-warming process. If he looked overly fragile or anaemic he would be considered incapable of bed warming. There were exceptions and he fondly spoke of a skeletal type traveller who literally burned up the sheets, such was the heat he radiated.

The most welcome type was a large well-fleshed, middle-aged male. Because of his proportions, this type of warmer flushed the cold out of every corner of the bed, thereby providing the legitimate owner of the bed with considerable leeway without the danger of cold, out-of-the-way corners. He could lie on back, belly or sides and stretch his toes to the utmost and be certain of natural warmth wherever he turned.

It was a fair exchange and my friend attributed his great age to this unique heating system. Women who do not share their husband's beds take note. Send him first to warm your bed before entering it.

I also remember a family in our street. One of the children was always sent upstairs at night to warm his grandmother's bed.

In the end, for all that may be said in favour of electric blankets and hot water bottles, there is nothing to equal the blissful heat of a partner's body after coming in from the cold of a winter night.

SOMNI BONKABIT PROFUNDIS

I AM OFTEN AMAZED at the quality of conversation in common or garden public houses. No one should show surprise if there is lofty conversation in pubs where poetry readings and book launchings are the norm for here one is likely to be confronted by intellectuals and assorted academics at every hand's turn. Here too are poets and poetesses who can confound and astonish. Yet, if you were to ask me, there is a richer vein of worthwhile comment where Joe Soaps and Jane Suds foregather.

Only the other evening in a hostelry I was privy to an exchange which deserves to be recalled. Nearby on two high stools sat two rather elderly chaps wearing caps and nursing pints. One suddenly raised his voice and stated that possession was nine points of the law.

A listener scoffed and asked, 'what the hell do you know about the law?'

'Nothing,' came the answer.

'But I heard you say that possession was nine points of the law?'

'No my friend,' came back the reply, 'what I said was that position was nine points of the law but I wasn't referring to law. I was referring to sex.'

A silence ensued. Customers came and went. The conversation resumed. The pair were now talking about poor relations. Again the same gentleman butted in.

'Your own is your own,' he said.

'Oh,' said the older of the elderly pair as he removed

his cap to blow his nose with a spotless white handkerchief, 'you'd never catch me blackguarding my poor relations. I'm always liberal with them. In fact I'd give them all away if I got someone to take them.'

The wittiest man I ever knew was educated in a pub. He had eschewed formal education and avoided school as though it were a dungeon.

'I learned how to read the clock in a pub,' he boasted, 'and newspapers and sums because there's adding and subtracting and multiplication going on all day in public houses all over the land.'

'What was the most memorable thing you ever heard in a pub?' I asked.

'Somni bonkabit profundis,' he answered at once.

'What does that mean?' I asked.

Solemnly he said – 'from a little sex comes deep sleep.'

In my own pub on Sunday night last we were talking about heaven, what it was like there and our chances of going there. One of our company who happens to be a chain-smoker, much to our disgust, interrupted the conversation by the simple expedient of lighting another cigarette. His concept of heaven he told us was Saint Peter ignoring non-smokers and offering cigarettes to those who did.

There is much to be gained form listening to conversations in public houses. One may learn free of charge and one may become a philosopher if he digests all he hears and absorbs all he sees.

One night I refused to serve a drunken visitor with the

pint he ordered.

'What town am I in?' he asked, confirming my esti-
mation of his condition.

'You're in the town of Listowel,' I informed him.

'Listowel!' he repeated the name in horror, 'I've heard
of it,' he said, 'it would make Sodom or Gomorrah look
like Lourdes.'

LOVE LIES BLEEDING

THERE IS A LATIN SAYING, the authorship of which escapes me right now. I always recall it during the aftermath of domestic upheavals especially those ones which are confined to husband and wife. The phrase, by the way, has just been attributed to Terence by a gin and tonic drinker who also happens to be something of a Latin scholar. Terence, as every publican knows, was brought by the Romans as a slave from Tarsus and wound up writing comedies until he was 25 years of age when he embarked on a voyage from which he did not return. *Amantium irae amoris integratis est.* Thus runs the observation, which means simply 'lovers quarrels are the renewal of love'. Oh, how true!

My first confirmation of the truth contained in this Roman adage occurred when I was quite a young man. As I was walking through a certain street in my native town a chamber pot whizzed past my head. It is difficult to describe the sound of a whizzing chamber pot but it differs from other whizzing objects in that it also whirrs and whistles as it whizzes past. I had a quick glimpse of the lady who threw the pot. She stood in the doorway of her house, her once beautiful face wrecked and dehumanised by the fury which she had brought upon herself. The scoundrel at whom the chamber pot had been aimed took refuge behind me as soon as he saw it in her hand. He had fled the confines of the martial battlefield in his pyjamas after being pelted with a half-full cocoa canister, a turnip and an alarm clock. These missiles were already strewn around our feet. I fled the scene but our friend stood his ground albeit at a safe distance.

That is the first chapter of the story. The second chapter begins an hour later as I am returning from my morning walk. I am astonished to see the lady who flung the aforementioned missile in the passionate embrace of the person who had managed to evade them. They kissed and cooed and cuddled and closed the door in my face with a bang as I passed.

How right was Terence the playwright. Earlier than that particular incident, however, there was another which deserves to be recalled. So far we may have deduced that reconciliation follows rows and we may also, therefore, deduce that there cannot be reconciliation without a row which brings me to the second incident.

Picture a busy fair day in a small town 40 years ago. The streets were chock-a-block with cattle and people. Among these people was an innocent farmer unused to the ways of the world. He had disposed of his cattle and was walking the streets lapping up the passing scene. Also among the throng was a travelling man and his wife. They were arguing when suddenly the male of the partnership seized the other by the hair of the head and brought her to the ground where he proceeded to strike her with open palm. The farmer was astonished to see that nobody inter-vened. This should have told him something but it didn't. Bravely he seized the traveller to restrain him. While thus occupied, the traveller's wife seized an iron kettle which happened to be hanging with other wares outside a hardware shop. One would imagine that she might seize the opportunity to get even with her husband. Alas, it was the unfortunate farmer to whom she enragedly addressed herself.

'Let him go, you streak of misery,' she shouted at the farmer and hit him with the kettle on top of the head, felling him at once.

Later when he woke up in hospital he had time to ponder on the foolishness of his action. As he was being taken away in the ambulance earlier, he saw that the tinker woman and her man were warmly embracing each other. He should have let well alone and allowed things to develop naturally. The traveller and his wife would have made it up anyway. They would have no other choice, just as the couple in the first incident had no other choice. He learned, poor fellow, that lovers quarrels are the renewal love and that he is a very foolish fellow who interferes with the course of custom.

Drinking Like a Horse

I HAVE ALWAYS HAD a tooth for beer and nearly always I knew when to draw the line. With whiskey it was different. With whiskey I had a relationship which was perilous to say the least. Once I got a taste of it I could hardly ever lay off. My whiskey-drinking period was when all the bad things happened to me. My career took a dip and my attitude was a disaster. However I faced up to the situation and went off the hard stuff.

I did not, however, go off the drink altogether. I returned to my more stable beer-drinking ways and I never returned to the hot stuff unless alone I needed a base for a cargo of beer at weddings or christenings or the like. I might have one or two to illuminate the interior so that the beer would take the right road.

Then I had an operation for the big C. I survived it and now, after three years of realignment and muscle building in the waterworks, I am able to hold my beer physically as well as mentally. In the process I discovered a great truth although I feel sure that there are some sensitive souls reading this who will not agree with me.

I discovered that there was infinitely more pleasure to be had from beer if one drank it naturally, that is to say not have to worry about the sound of drinking. When I first started making noises as I drank my beer about three months ago I found people looking at me in the bars I frequent and in my own bar in particular which is quite understandable since my own bar is the bar I frequent the most.

I think it gives the customer confidence if he sees the proprietor of a bar sampling his own wares. Omar Khayyam put it another way when he wrote:

I often wonder what the vintners buy
One half so precious as the goods they sell.

I remember one occasion after I had swallowed copiously from my pint glass to hear one customer saying to another 'he drinks like a horse'.

I felt flattered since I love horses and I have heard horses drinking when they are truly thirsty. They relish their drinks and they make apologies to none for the sloshing and the spluttering, the swashing and the deluging, the swirling and the drenching. All the horse is doing is showing full appreciation for that which slakes his thirst. If a horse can do it I told myself why can't I or to put it another way, if Caligula the Roman emperor could make a consul out of his horse why can't John B. Keane make a horse out of himself!

It sounded logical at the time and I make no apologies. I persevered with my noisy drinking and I swear that the drink tastes twice as good and moreover a drinking companion of mine, recently converted, says that he never before enjoyed beer so much. When I was younger I used to make noise drinking my soup and so did we all but we were cautioned by our parents and we drank our soup without making any noise. We lost much as a result. I realise that it is now too late for me to make noise drinking my soup. I might only frighten my grandchildren and terrorise the womenfolk of the house.

With beer it's different and it's going to remain different and if you come across me in some tavern making noise over my beer you mind your own business and drink your beer your way. Just let me drink my beer my way.

My only regret is that I spent so much of an otherwise colourful lifetime being a slave to convention. Just because everybody is doing something does not mean that it is right.

I never knew the real taste of beer till I started drinking like a horse. I don't make as much noise but I make a proportionate amount and over the past few months nobody in the bar relishes their beer the way I do apart, of course, from my one convert although I swear I am beginning to hear the first faint sibilances of snorts and the first weak stutters of mature spluttering from other drinkers which indicate more horsy drinkers in the course of time.

THE KINGDOM OF KERRY

ADDRESSING THE OLD HOUSE of Parliament in Dublin in 1793, the great Irish advocate, John Philpot Curran, commented adversely that the magistracy of the county of Kerry were so opposed to the laws of the land that they were a 'law unto themselves, a Kingdom apart'. The name stuck and at balls and banquets thereafter the Kingdom was toasted roundly. In fact there are many Kerrymen who say there are only two real Kingdoms, the Kingdom of God and the Kingdom of Kerry.

Among other things this Kingdom contains the next European parish to America which is Ballinskelligs in the south-west. Then there is Killarney of the lakes, Tralee of the Roses and Listowel of the Writers. The county is distinguished by a gossamer-like lunacy which is addictive but not damaging. Tralee is its capital and a worthy one it is, often called the gateway to Kerry and hosts annually the great Festival of Kerry without equal anywhere in the world.

Kerry contains dell and crag and mountain and a thousand vistas of unbelievable beauty. There is hardly a roadside where the ever-changing chortling of a fishful stream cannot be heard. Then there is the towering, chattering, sometimes silent Atlantic which washes the shores of Kerry from Ballybunion golf links, beloved of Tom Watson, to Kenmare.

Ballybunion is beautiful beyond compare. What does one say about the champagne air and the daunting cliffs of

Doon that has not already been said! Perhaps a tale from the past will serve better than an avalanche of laudatory adjectives from the present. Let us go back to the time of the Fianna, pre-Christian guardians of Ireland's shores.

Imagine young Oisin the poet, his chieftain father Fionn and a few more of the Fianna indulging in one of their less-favourite pursuits, i.e., assisting in the saving of hay for one of the local farmers. The meadow in question lies halfway between Listowel and Ballybunion. Overhead there is a clear sky and a balmy breeze blows inland from the nearby Atlantic. The time would be the end of June.

Suddenly out of the distance comes the thunder of hooves. The Fianna, no less fond of diversion than any other voluntary labourers, lean on their wooden hay rakes and wait for the horse and, hopefully, rider to come within their ken. They have not long to wait for immediately they are confronted by the comeliest of maidens astride a snorting white charger.

No cap or cloak, as the song says, does this maiden wear but her long flowing tresses of burnished gold cover the sensitive areas of her beautifully shaped body. Standing erect on her steed she surveys the menfolk all around and a doughty bunch they are, each man more robust and more handsome than the next. No interest does she evince as her blue eyes drift from face to face. Then her gaze alights on Oisin, poet, philosopher, charmer and athlete. She surveys him for a long time before she gives him the come hither. He hesitates.

'Come on,' she says.

'Where?' asks Oisin.

'Tir na nÓg,' says she.

'Go on man,' urge the Fianna in unison. No grudge do they bear him for such was the code of the Fianna.

He hesitates no longer but throws his hay rake to one side and, with a mighty bound, lands himself behind her on the back of the magnificent white steed.

'Gup outa that,' says she and the next thing you know they have gone from view.

'Where did she say they were going?' old Fionn asks anxiously.

'Tir na nÓg,' the others answer, 'the land of the ever young.'

Then one day, fifty years later, at that part of the Listowel-Ballybunion road known as Gortnaskeha the white horse reappeared bearing upon its back the handsome Oisin and the beautiful blonde. They came upon a number of men trying to move a large boulder from one side of the road to the other. All their efforts were in vain. Oisin leaned down from the horse and with his little finger moved the great stone to one side but, in so doing, fell to the ground.

As he lay there he changed from a lusty youth to a withered old man in a matter of moments. The blonde flicked the reins and was never seen again in that part of the world although other blondes would surface in Ballybunion with unfailing regularity year after year down to this very day and everyone of them as lovely and dangerous as Niamh of the Golden Hair, which was the name of

Oisin's partner.

Finding himself unable to rise Oisin placed a hand on the shoulder of one of the Gortnaskeha men.

'I've been in Tir na nÓg,' he said.

'Tir na nÓg!' they exclaimed in wonder for all had heard of it.

'Tir na nÓg, my tail,' said an old man with a pipe in his mouth. 'Ballybunion he's been to!'

'But how did he age so much?' the others asked.

'Listen my friend,' said the old man, 'if you spent a weekend in Ballybunion with a blonde like that you'd look fifty years older too and you'd have wrinkles galore.'

Which all goes to prove that a long weekend in Ballybunion can knock more out of a man than a score of years anywhere else.

Nearby is my native, beautiful Listowel, serenaded night and day by the gentle waters of the River Feale, Listowel where it is easier to write than not to write, where life is leisurely, where first love never dies and the tall streets hide the loveliness, the heartbreak and the moods, great and small of all the gentle souls of a great and good community. Sweet, incomparable home town that shaped and made me.

Killarney is the gateway to the south-west of the Kingdom and so beauteous and captivating are the vistas thereafter that one is lost without a loving companion to share the pain and the hurt that great beauty induces. Without the love of my heart beside me I, personally, am lost here.

In 1842, at the age of 32 Tennyson wrote about this

enchanted region:

> The splendour falls on castle walls,
> And snowy summits old in story
> The long light shakes across the lakes
> And the wild cataract leaps in glory.

Tennyson knew and loved Kerry. Kerry, however, is as much its people as anything else. Once, years ago, in my native town of Listowel, I listened to an overheated preacher as he ranted and raved about the declining morals of Kerry folk. On my way from church I asked an elderly friend what he thought of the sermon.

'His fulminations will have the same effect on the morals of Kerry people as the droppings of an underfed blackbird on the water levels of the Grand Coulee Dam,' he said.

The Kerry attitude to life is spiced with sarcasm and humour. There is a jaundiced undertone to all our observations and we have a fine contempt for pomp and vanity. Other counties joke about us but they must not be taken seriously for what is a hyper-critical county after all but an organisation that revels in its own imagined supremacy and, to cover its inadequacies, frequently makes cheap jokes at the expense of its more talented neighbours.

Long, dull sentences, especially religious and political, are anathema to the true Kerryman. The well-made, craftily-calefacted comment, the stinging riposte and the verbal arrows of cold truth will always penetrate the armour of cant and hypocrisy in the eyes of Kerry people.

We tend to digress as well but we do so for a purpose.

Kerry folk know that there is no such thing as a truly straight furrow or a simple answer. Our digressions are what oases are to desert nomads, what incidental levities are to pressurised, underpaid workers. To a Kerryman life without digressions is like a thoroughfare without side streets.

I might write about other aspects of Kerry such as its fishing and its horse racing (over twenty days in all) or I might outline for you the course of a particularly well-taken goal from boot to goal posts but I think it's more important that we concentrate on the living lingo of the Greater, Hardnecked Atlantical Warbler known as the Kerryman who quests individually and in flocks for all forms of diversion and is to be found high and low, winter and summer, wherever there is the remotest prospect of drink, sex, confusion or commotion.

He loves his pub and he loves his pint and he will tell you that the visitor, no matter where he hails from, is always at home in the Kingdom. He is hospitable to a fault but he eschews everyday language. I remember only last November to have been involved in an argument about the value of a trailer-load of peat for my winter fires. A countryman friend, in order to bring down the price, spoke disparagingly of the trailer's contents.

'A young sparrow,' said he, 'would carry more in its beak'.

Then there was the Kerryman in a Dublin hotel who was given fat rashers for his breakfast: 'There wasn't,' said he, 'as much lean in them as you'd draw with a solitary stroke of a red biro!'

There is no such entity, by the way, as a conventional Kerryman. If you try to analyse him he generates confusion. He will not be pinned down and you have as much chance of getting a straight answer from a cornered Kerryman as you have of getting a goose egg from an Arctic tern.

Your true Kerryman loves words, however, and that's a sure way to get him going. Snare him with well-chosen words and outrageous phrases and he will respond, especially if he's intoxicated, with sempiternal sentences, sonorous and even supernatural. On the other hand he has the capacity for long, perplexing silences. It is when he is speechless, however, that he is at his most dangerous. He is weighing up the opposition, waiting for an opening, so that he can demoralise you.

One evening last summer as I sat outside a pub in the shadow of Beenatee Mountain in Cahersiveen, the old Gaelic teacher with whom I had been drinking for most of the afternoon told me that the reason Kerryman were so articulate was because the elements were their real mentors. 'They can patter like rain,' said he, 'roar like thunder, foam like the sea, sigh like the wind and on top of all that you'll never catch one of us boasting.'

Kerry's two great peninsulas provide a topographic mix which no guide book, atlas nor survey map can adequately convey. There are mountain lakes and waterfalls, mysterious inlets, sheer cliffs and golden beaches, breathtaking in their vastness where often I have not encountered another human in the round of a summer's day. The peninsulas of Kerry are only half discovered. Everywhere along your route are tiny roads leading to secret slips and piers and periwinkle-studded rocks where the bright water laps and laves. The flatlands of the Maharees on the Dingle peninsula boasts Fermoyle strand which is over-shadowed by Mount Brandon, called after Brendan the Navigator, patron saint of Kerry and discoverer of America whatever the Spanish might say.

Schools of dolphin traverse the adjacent seas and oc-casionally stand on their tails on the water to execute their own Irish jigs when they spot humans on terra firma. If you wish you can make the acquaintance of Dingle's own resi-dent dolphin, Fungi, by simply hiring a boat.

This is a landscape I know and love. Where else could I walk a golden strand for an entire afternoon in my pelt in the certainty that I am safe from prying eyes. As a pre-caution I carry bathing togs on top of my head but rarely anywhere else! The Ring of Kerry takes in the peninsula of Iveragh as well as other smaller peninsulas – dotted with quaint coves, rock pools and comfortable pubs that special-ise in fresh seafood and friendly staff ready to adopt the stranger. From the windows of these amiable establish-ments one can watch the ebbing and flowing of the tides in comfort.

The towns of Kenmare, Cahersiveen, Waterville and Sneem are all on the Ring of Kerry route and I stay some-times at the Lansdowne Arms in Kenmare where the land-lord will sing with me and his other customers in the bliss-ful Kerry night. Away from the golden sands are sally-fringed streams, rivers and lakes where one can enjoy a preview of paradise and rare moments of sublime tranquillity.

I recall many such glorious occasions and one in particular, a little way from Dingle town with its fishing fleets and elegant streets, no two of which are alike. It was that time of evening when light resigns itself to half light, yielding finally to darkness and it seemed that all nature was aware that stillness was needed if honourable surrender was to take place. Only in Kerry, with its magical retreats, can one experience such peace.

There is an achingly beautiful road between Kenmare and Sneem which takes you along the shore of Kenmare Bay past Templenoe and Parknasilla where Shaw wrote *Saint Joan*.

Being born in Kerry, in my opinion, is the greatest gift that God can bestow on any man. When you belong to Kerry you know you have a head start on the other fellow. You don't boast about it and you never crow about it. You just know, because of your geographical location, that you are IT. You are the bee's knees. You really don't need any other assets. You need no great talents, no heavy financing.

One thing it doesn't give you is respectability but that's the last thing a true Kerryman wants. Knowing where you belong outweighs respectability any day. In belonging to Kerry you belong to the elements, to the spheres spinning in their heavens. You belong to history and language, romance and ancient song. It's almost unbearable being a Kerrymen and it's an awesome responsibility!

CORNER BOY CHAMPIONSHIP

WHEN I AIRED THE idea in the pub the other night it was dismissed by all save one. 'We'll have a championship,' I suggested, 'an all-Ireland competition to discover the champion Irish corner boy.'

While I am not comparing the Christian to the animal for one minute let me say that there are successful dog shows and successful horse shows and usen't there be an agricultural show in Listowel with competitions for hens and ducks and the like.

'He's right,' said the man who had agreed with me, 'are there not beauty competitions and strong men competitions every other day and everybody takes them for granted. I think an all-Ireland for corner boys is a marvellous idea.'

Greatly heartened by his support I pointed out to him that the first championship should take place at the corner right in the middle of the town.

He responded with an adamantine shaking of the head.

'You fool you,' said a Ballybunion man who had shot down the idea in the first place, 'your man has a corner house of his own with a run-down business and this is his chance to salvage it.'

Words could not express my disillusionment. How crass can man be! There I was thinking I had a convert to the artistic side of corner boying when all I really had was a man who wanted to put his own interests first.

I am, however, a man who is never downcast for long and that is why I am here right now to plead my case. Perhaps there are readers who might be interested in the idea of an all-Ireland corner boy championship and in the course of time a world corner boy championship. It need not be the corner across the road. My motives are lofty and not perverted by greed or gain of any kind. In fact I would go so far as to sponsor the first championship and at a venue selected by a specially-formed committee of people who are interested in the make-up and in the antics of corner boys. We might even invite a few well-known corner boys from a variety of towns and villages and hear what they have to say. Perhaps one or two might supplement our judging panel to ensure that the highest standards are attained. We would draw up a list of the finer points of the classical corner boy, to include stance, disposition, endurance and of course, sobriety.

Let me say at once that there is no such a person as a drunken corner boy. Any self-respecting corner boy will tell you that drink is absolutely out if one is to perform his corner boy duties with authority and distinction. The chief function of a corner boy is simply to be present. A corner boy must never, never concern himself with the troubles of the world and must never, never act as witness in a court case or dispute. He must vanish like a mist in case he is called upon to take sides.

'But,' the gentle reader will ask, 'what does he do?'

The answer, of course, is that he reassures. Suppose, for instance, a nervous female is apprehensive about some aspect of human activity in the vicinity of the corner it is the function of the corner boy to be reassuring and to dispel her worries by simply being there.

SINCE I WROTE ABOUT the possibility of holding a national and, maybe later, an international championship for corner boys I have received some encouraging letters and some discouraging ones as well. One of the latter, not quite without foundation, deserves to be quoted from.

'Why not,' writes FAIR PLAY, 'a championship for drunken writers or even talkative writers because that's all I ever see and hear when I come to Writers' Week?'

Point taken FAIR PLAY, point taken. Maybe when we finish with the corner boy championships we'll do as you suggest and maybe, since you are so anxious for such events to take place, you might provide your name and address so that we can consult with you about rules and regulations.

Despite what people have been led to believe by ethnographers that, for instance, corner boys are like Greek choruses, that they are outside the drama so to speak, the corner boy nevertheless has many functions. The corner boy for instance is a verifier. He rarely answers questions such as where is the post office or where is the public toilet but should you say to him 'is the post office up this way?' he may very well nod the head in verification.

You must never ask him a straight question for if he answers he may become involved and that is why a corner boy is a corner boy in the first place. He does not want to participate. He is, however, sometimes prepared to give the nod as for instance when the biggest liar in the community is relating a really outsized whopper to an innocent victim. The liar will sometimes turn to the corner boy for verification. It is not always forthcoming but depending on the humour of the corner boy in question the liar may win his approval because the corner boy sees the liar as an enemy of the establishment and therefore worthy of his support.

I remember one particular occasion when a stout woman bearing a large bag of groceries slipped on a banana skin and fell to the ground, her groceries scattered far and wide. The corner boy did not come to her aid. He could not because of his position, because of his status, a status which has been conferred on him by right of long tenure. He did not ignore the fallen woman. He signalled to a passer-by that there was a lady in distress and nodded his approval when the passer-by went to the woman's aid. The good Samaritan did not merely content himself with lifting the woman to her feet. He also gathered her scattered groceries, returning each item to the empty bag, each item that is with the exception of an orange which had rolled almost as far as the corner boy's feet and there wobbled momentarily before taking up residence. As the good Samaritan bent to retrieve the orange the corner boy deftly place a leg lightly on same. Both men nodded respectfully at each other and when the good Samaritan and the fallen woman had departed upon their separate ways the corner boy bent and lifted the orange. First he rubbed it against his sleeve to remove any contamination which might have attached itself to the skin. Then he put it in his pocket with a view to addressing himself to this unexpected titbit when safe from the public gaze. It was his entitlement. The way he looked at it was that, if he had not alerted the passer-by, the fallen woman would have remained on the flat of her back until Gabriel tootled his horn on judgement day. Is it not well known that we live in an age where Samaritans have become as scarce as dodos!

So you see gentle reader that the corner boy is not a mere propper of corners nor is he at the corner for his own delight and benefit. He is there to give the nod to all that is wholesome and beneficial to himself and to mankind and how many can say that they have served in such a fashion without hope of reward in this vale of tears.

BLACK EYES

IF, AS WE ARE told violence is on the increase then where have all the black eyes gone? I have not seen a comprehensive black eye in years and you might say that I am the sort of chap who is perpetually on the lookout for such colourful disfigurations of the physiognomy.

I received my first black eye when I was fourteen. It was unsolicited. A school bully, the last one I was to encounter, introduced himself one day on the football pitch by extending his right fist in the direction of my left eye. The discolouration lasted for weeks. At first I was ashamed but as the days went by I started to attract attention and statements started to circulate, statements such as 'You should see the other fellow' and 'that's the blackest black eye I ever saw'.

Now with hindsight I have to concede that it was worth it all if only for the notoriety it brought me not to mention the stares of impressionable girls. A genuine black eye or rather the surrounds of the eye should really be multi-coloured with a basic puce and outbreaks of yellow, black and red like Shelley's autumn leaves. If the eye proper was a little bloodshot it only added to the appeal. In no time at all I was comparing my black eye with other black eyes and I am proud to be able to say that mine was easily the ugliest of that season's crop.

I heard a teacher say regarding that black eye of mine 'It's a poor school that hasn't a black eye or two to show for itself'. There I was then, the showpiece of the school you might say when this pretender to my throne suddenly hove out of nowhere boasting two black eyes mind you. He couldn't do with one, the scoundrel, the same as any normal schoolboy. It had to be two. In no time at all the spotlight was turned away from me. I had two eyes all right the same as he had but one of mine was white. My one black eye was also as colourful as his two black eyes together but that counted for nothing in the eyes of the juvenile onlookers. Two of anything was better than one as far as the school was concerned.

Looking back now on that black eye I must say that it attracted more attention than say a broken hand or a broken leg and if you don't believe me just ask yourself how long since you were diverted by crutches or bandages. There's no town at the moment without several casualties bandaged to the utmost, many of the victims waiting for compensation to set in.

A black eye is different. If a man or a boy walks down the street with a black eye he'll draw more stares than Lady Godiva drew during her legendary ride through Coventry. That is because black eyes have become scarcer than nude women in public places.

A man with a black eye, of course, was never really as black as he was painted. A saintly man was as likely to receive a black eye as a sinner during a time when men of pugilistic disposition never resorted to weapons.

I have heard of eyes that were as black as soot, as black as sin, as black as ink, as black as coal and as black as the pit to mention but a few. The reality is that a black eye is

34

pucer than it is black. If you must wound me or mark or disfigure me in any way give me a black eye any day. Let us conclude with a short extract from Charles Coborn's song:

Two lovely black eyes,
Oh what a surprise!
Only for telling a chap he was wrong,
Two lovely black eyes.

HIGH EXPECTATIONS

ONCE UPON A TIME, many years ago, a woman came to housekeep for us on a temporary basis. Our regular house-keeper dislocated her ankle alighting from a Bingo bus. The newcomer proved to be capable and efficient and all went well for awhile. Then for no reason that we could fathom she upped and departed without as much as a day's notice. When my wife asked her why she was leaving she said she couldn't stick it. No, it wasn't anything either of us said or did and it wasn't the wages.

We would not discover the reasons for her premature departure until our regular housekeeper returned. It emer-ged that her replacement was seriously disillusioned with myself.

'I thought,' she confided to our regular housekeeper, 'that he'd be going around all day talking to himself.'

'Talking to himself!' our regular echoed incredulously, 'what in God's name would he go doing a thing like that for!'

'Well,' said the other, 'I thought he'd be cracking all kinds of jokes when all he would do was lock himself into a room and bang away at that oul' typewriter all day. Sure no one could stick that.'

Our regular housekeeper was befuddled. She decided to question her replacement more closely. After consider-able probing it transpired that she had ulterior motives. 'I saw myself,' she confided, 'sitting down with a reporter and writing a book about him and about his antics. You know what they say about him don't you?'

'No,' said our housekeeper, 'I don't but I'd like to.'

'Well, that he does be all the time effin' and blindin' and boozin' and singin' and entertainin'.'

'If he does,' said our regular, 'I never noticed it.'

'Well can you ever tell about a person!' said the disgruntled replacement, 'and there I was thinkin' he was a right hoor entirely.'

Time passed and I found myself in a public house in Ballybunion. It was the liveliest hour of the night and closing time was fast approaching. My companions, equally intoxicated, prevailed upon me to sing. I was asked for an encore and delivered. Afterwards as I indulged in a richly-deserved swallow from the pint which had been provided by an admirer I received a thump in the back which caused me to splutter.

'You're a gas bloody man aren't you!' said the man who had delivered the thump. Hatred flashed in his eyes and his normally ugly mug turned even uglier. Mystified I asked him to explain himself.

'Ah yes!' he said bitterly, 'you sing for big shots all right but not a note for my poor wife.'

Still mystified I placed my pint to one side and intimated that I would not be above implanting a solid kick on his hostile posterior if he persisted in his belligerent advances. One of my friends threatened him with the civic guards but this nettled him even more. Suddenly there was a bellicose female standing by his side. You guessed it. It was the very woman who had acted as a replacement for our regular housekeeper.

'You won't treat me like dirt,' she was saying or words to that effect. The upshot of the ruction was that I departed the scene rather than fan the flames of an ugly row.

The moral here is, of course, that the expectations of the replacement housekeeper were too high and we all know where high expectations lead but just in case you don't I'll tell you. They lead to disaster. How blessed is she or he who has a built-in system of self-entertainment and who has not to depend upon fickle creatures such as myself for diversion.

SEEING THINGS

AND NOW, A WORD or two about seeing things. I draw upon the saying 'One Swallow doesn't make a Summer' or, if you like, one kiss does not make a romance.

Anyway to proceed and to begin with as the song says, my mother and I were once walking through the grove of Gurtenard in my native town when our ears were unexpectedly assailed by female laughter. It brightened the woodlands and flushed a drowsy blackbird from his arboreal hideaway. He was a fine bird and he was very annoyed if one was to believe his protestations. We came upon the girls as they sauntered happily and blithely without a care in the world at that particular time. Care never leaves us alone for long and will return to pester us no matter how high we climb the ladder of ecstasy.

Unaware of our presence the girls stood stock still for a moment, embraced gently and kissed. I was roughly ten years of age at the time but young as I was it had come to my ears that there were girls who kissed each other on a regular basis. It was a far less enlightened climate than now.

'Look,' I said to my mother, 'two girls kissing.'

She nodded, having already noted the situation. She sauntered onwards without speaking. I was surprised because she had always been prepared to comment on anything and everything. Then the girls disappeared from view around a bend. My mother paused.

'Could be,' she said matter-of-factly, 'that they are learning how to kiss and must practise with each other for the want of a boyfriend. That way they'll be ready when a boyfriend comes along.'

For the time and place it was a good answer. I never saw those girls again but I have a feeling they are happy somewhere.

Then there was the Sunday afternoon my father and I went walking in the same area. It was wintertime and birds were scarce on the ground and in the air. There was a deep silence in the grove due to the absence of a breeze. Then there was some shouting and the sound of running footsteps. We paused and beheld two young men, one wearing goggles and the other a leather visor.

'Where are their motor bikes?' I asked my father.

'They are not bikers,' my father informed me.

I remember having pressed him for an answer of some kind. 'They are rugby players,' he explained.

I let it go at that. Something in the trees overhead distracted me. Maybe it was the beginning of a breeze. It would be some time before I fully comprehended why rugby players would be wearing goggles and visors. It did not happen really until I found myself in a similar predicament. The goggles and visor were disguises. If the young men in question had been identified they would undoubtedly be suspended from playing Gaelic football for such was the law of the time. If a Gaelic footballer played rugby or attended a rugby dance he would be suspended by his club from playing the native games. There were extreme feelings in the air at the time and, when certain things are in the air, issues get clouded. Vision gets clouded as well.

So we see how easy it is to be mistaken and how simple it is to deduce wrong impressions. We see too how things change with the passage of time and how today's virtue was often yesterday's transgression.

SHIFTY PATTERS

NEWS LATELY OF AN outbreak of posterior-patting in several public houses in the neighbourhood. It is extremely difficult to identify posterior patters or indeed posterior pinchers. When the desecrated female turns round in order to see who has patted her there may be several males in the vicinity. Alas and alack she tends to absolve the man with the innocent face and directs her wrath in the direction of the seemingly hardened character. In almost all cases she is wrong for it is the man with the innocent, often angelic, face who pats the most when opportunity presents itself.

I spoke to a publican recently and when I asked him to comment on the outbreak he told me that, of late, several suspicious-looking continentals have been frequenting his pub after sessions in local golf courses. 'Continentals,' said he, 'are the shiftiest posterior patters in the world. They pat with uncanny speed but if they do they still manage to cover the entire pattable area with delicacy and skill so that in some instances the victims cannot be certain whether they have been patted or not.'

I do not agree that Continentals are shiftier posterior patters than for instance Irish posterior patters. They may be faster but they are choosy whereas your average Irish posterior patter will pat anything regardless of size or shape.

As I pondered on the problem in the pub on a recent Sunday night a woman leaped from her place at the counter clutching her behind. At first I thought she had been pinched and I was highly annoyed for pinching is crude and nasty and deserving of swift retribution. As she was to say herself later she had only been patted. When she searched for her assailant she concluded that it had to be one of three males who had been standing directly behind her in the crowded bar.

Two of the males were from the Continent and the other was a countryman who calls once in a blue moon. The victim immediately accused the Continentals and referred in the most unkindly fashion to the dubiancy of their ancestry suggesting that they had been mothered by she apes and fathered by donkeys. They listened in amazement and then they quit the scene without finishing their drinks which means that they must have been terrified because I will say this for Continentals – if they have paid for their drinks they will always finish them. The distressed victim meanwhile accepted the brandy which I poured her and looked everywhere around for sympathy which came her way in abundance. The countryman who stood behind her clenched his teeth and his otherwise placid features contorted themselves into a snarl.

'If I had a gun,' said he, 'I'd blow their brains out.'

Eventually we placated the victim and she deposited the patted commodity on a convenient stool the better to protect herself should the Continentals return. Soon everybody was singing as is the wont of the clientele on Sunday nights. Then in the middle of *Danny Boy* a woman leapt into the middle of the arena clutching her posterior. Somebody had patted her on the you-know-where without her permission. Immediately a stranger who had been nursing a rum and coke for several minutes previous to the attack on the lady's extremity disappeared without a word, forgetting to close the door behind him. An irate posse started to assemble with a view to pursuit. Fortunately a local farmer intervened.

'Ye would be hanging an innocent man,' he insisted. 'The man gone out that door kept his hands on his drink all the time he was here.'

Then his voice fell and we gathered round. The farmer informed us that it was the innocent-looking countryman who had done the patting.

'He was like greased lightning,' said the farmer, 'one minute his hands were clutching her posterior and the next minute they were back in his pockets and all while you'd be saying pat.'

When we looked round there was no sign of the countryman. Like a thief in the night he had slipped away, another innocent posterior added to his long list.

I called his face to mind that very night and I was forced to conclude that we had been blaming the Continentals in the wrong. They were nothing more and nothing less than innocent victims of blind justice. Our own fellow countryman was the real villain of the piece and hadn't he all the classic points of the true posterior patter! There was the large Adam's apple, the dark eyes and the angelic face. There was the timid mouth in which you would think butter would not melt but that same mouth as we now know would melt rod iron. He had the simple smile which is the chief characteristic of bottom pinchers and posterior patters everywhere. Your authentic, dyed-in-the wool posterior patter has one outstanding feature and it is that he doesn't look in the least like a posterior patter. If you were to put him in a room with a hundred of his victims not one would pick him out.

I have learned a few simple truths about posterior patters in my time and I believe the time has come to divulge them in the interests of humanity as a whole. I am convinced that we are all potential posterior patters, even the sanest of us and the safest of us and the most restrained of us. Given the right moment or the right occasion an otherwise normal man can be transformed into a posterior patter without his consent.

Even a man who is pure of heart and says his prayers at night can be turned into a posterior patter when the moon changes although, to be fair, we cannot lay the full blame on the moon. The object which has been patted must take a small portion of the blame but only a very, very small portion. I once heard a man say that certain female posteriors were made to be patted just as surely as water attracts ducks.

We have not had an outbreak of posterior patting in this part of the world for several years now and I wonder what could have brought on the present one. Sometimes I look in the mirror and I look for telltale signs, the flicker of an eyelid, the twitch of a lip, anything that might forewarn me of the awful transformation which has befallen so many stout-hearted, innocent men. Do not smirk gentle reader.

No man is immune. You could be next.

THEN I WAS INFORMED by an elderly man that posterior patting is not the debased act I make it out to be. Let me say at once that I did not refer to posterior patting as a debased act. Why should I or how could I when inside every member of the male species is the potential for posterior patting! Even the pure of heart, as I said, are not immune from the urge to pat when resolve weakens and the steadiest of disciplines waver.

Anyway what this elderly gentleman said to me is interesting. 'I have been patting posteriors for years but I do not regard it as sinful or criminal. My chief reason for patting female posteriors is to calm the women in question,' he told me.

He went on to explain that he frequently laid hands on female posteriors in order to steady or compose their proprietresses in times of stress or danger. It had, apparently, always a beneficial effect and after a reassuring, steadying pat the patted females always calmed down.

'I can understand,' said he 'how women might be frightened or intimidated by a clumsy pat or a crude pinch but an experienced patter like myself knows exactly the right amount to dispense.'

I remember when I was a garsún in Ballybunion during the Second World War there were many women who wore bathing togs made of flour bags. Written on the bottom of some togs was the legend 'Do Not Pat or Thump'. This was not written to keep molesters at bay. Rather it was

46

printed on the flour bags when they stood full and inviting outside the doors of flour and meal merchants. *Do Not Pat* meant that if one patted the full flour bag, clouds of flour would be sent flying wastefully here, there and everywhere whereas if one patted the posterior covered by the flour bag in question the only reaction would be clouds of invective.

Not all posterior patters are reprobates our roués. Some regard themselves as human benefactors of the highest order. 'There are certain females who need to have their behinds patted on a regular basis,' a distant relation of mine announced lately, 'and I feel it is my duty to pat all inviting posteriors within my ken. Women can't very well ask men to pat them so that I regard it as my right to do the needful whenever possible.'

There are many like this kind-hearted soul and although they act from the loftiest motives their unselfish ministrations are frequently misunderstood. They have had their faces slapped, their jaws clocked, their shins kicked and without mention of other anatomical parts they have generally been badly treated through no fault of their own.

Different with the cowardly wretch who pats and pinches females posteriors for perverse purposes known only to himself. Why he should select this inoffensive, tender, bewitching area for such contempt is beyond me. A convicted posterior patter, a real habitual, was overheard in a pub recently saying that the female posterior was the most provocative of all objects known to the human eye. He would justify his rotten behaviour on this observation alone.

'I find them irresistible,' he said, 'and my only hope of salvation is to go around with my eyes closed.'

The real villain of the entire piece is the scoundrel who nips in for a quick pinch or pat which takes his victim completely by surprise. Before she has time to turn round and remonstrate he has disappeared into thin air and as a result an innocent man who never patted a behind in his life is often subjected to a torrent of abuse or even physical assault.

What is the solution? I honestly don't know. Women can't very well go around with 'Do Not Pat' signs on their behinds. Maybe a hidden beeper might be the job. The unwanted patter would be caught red-handed and knight errants in the vicinity might come to the lady's aid.

DOGS

NOW I'D LIKE TO mention dogs. However, let me say that I am not addressing myself merely to dog-lovers or dog-fanciers. This address is to all manner of people from those who cannot abide dogs to those who prefer cats or budgies and even to lion-tamers and their wives and families. Dog-lovers and fanciers are free to read it if they so wish but only as long as they remember that it is not addressed exclusively to them. Having made this clear we are now free to proceed.

My dog, if I had one, would be a wire-haired terrier of set ways and agreeable disposition. The reason I don't keep a dog at this present time is that my last two, both innocent pups, were stolen from me by dog thieves. The last fully-grown dog I owned was what we who are not experts loosely call a sheep dog. He was afraid of rats and mice but great as was his fear of these he was even more afraid of other dogs.

'Don't get him going,' said the man who sold him to me, 'because there's no tiger his master.'

He sat outside our door for a good many contented, untroubled years with a reputation for ferocity that grew with his age. He would look dreamily up and down the street and when cross dogs approached with suspicious sniffs and provocative snarls he would immediately close his eyes and pretend to be asleep. Aggressive dogs who invaded his territory got the impression that he just couldn't be bothered, that he didn't have to prove himself, that he was a dog to be avoided.

Luckily for him he had a fighter's face, scarred and bruised from investigating empty canisters and broken jampots. This alone was often sufficient to intimidate those dogs who are forever on the lookout for a good fight.

He died young as dogs go but I was led to believe that this was due to lack of exercise because while other dogs barked in anticipatory delight whenever their master appeared equipped for a stroll in the countryside my dog was nowhere to be found.

Still I like dogs because all dogs, like human beings, are bluffers, and no two are alike. I always salute dogs with whom I am acquainted, that is to say the dogs of neighbours and the dogs of friends. None of these has ever saluted me back. Some I have saluted sidled away self-consciously while others followed me for long distances as if the salute were a command to accompany me.

I have a brother who was followed by dogs all his life and during his first visit to the city he was followed aboard a bus by two common curs who could not possibly have known him because he had never been in the city before. When he found a permanent position in the capital he would go for long walks on fine evenings. Always he would be followed home to the door of his lodgings by one or more dogs. There was something in his makeup which held a special appeal for dogs. Cross dogs never barked at him and would follow him instead, respectfully, to the farthest boundaries of their bailiwicks, assuring his well-being and privacy as it were until he passed into some other canine's domain.

When the brother started to do a bit of a line with a good-looking girl who worked in the same building the dogs became an embarrassment. Whenever he took her for a walk he was followed by a dog or two. There was a particular mongrel of heterogeneous breeding predominantly Alsatian and Greyhound who used to lie in wait for him in doorways near his place of employment. In the end he was forced to leave the building by a rear exit. At the back entrance there would always be others to take the place of the one at the front.

Once while strolling in Stephen's Green where he frequently went to admire the ducks and find a measure of peace from the turmoil of the metropolis some instinct told him to look to his rear. At the time he was in the company of a new girl having long before broken off negotiations with the first one. Close on his heels there was a small, sad-looking terrier who persisted in dogging him no matter what direction he might take. He became justifiably annoyed and started to fling stones at his pursuer but the dog refused to go away. Again and again the same sort of situation arose. There he would be walking in some pleasant place with a girl when a dog would appear at his heels and remain there till he reached the safety of his lodgings.

Then one evening a friend told him how the problem might be overcome.

'Get a dog of your own,' he suggested. He then explained that those dogs who were in the habit of following him did so in the hope that he might adopt one of them. 'When they see you with a dog of your own,' his friend assured him, 'they will leave you in peace'.

So he got himself a dog, a genuine 'five-eights'. A five-eights is a dog with five parts of a true breed and three parts of all sorts. Personally speaking, I know dogs who have as many as ten different breeds apparent in their dispositions and physical characteristics.

I am seriously thinking of getting a dog again. I am in the market for a quiet, efficient fellow who would like to take up employment in a home where prospects are good and where there is every hope of advancement. Canvassing will disqualify.

Too Serious

IT WOULD HAVE BEEN in the mid-1930s. I would have been a garsún, a mere nipper. A good-looking girl arrived to work in one of the local boarding houses and was noticed immediately by an agricultural worker employed by an uncle of mine who kept a large number of milch cows. The cows were driven home every morning and evening from the town's outlying fields and were milked in a long shed at the rear of the dwelling house a few doors from where I lived. We shall call the agricultural worker by the name of Rest because he never rested.

'Give her this note,' he said to me one evening, 'and let me know what she says.'

I delivered the note and awaited a reply. She took her time and read the note a second time. I also had a look at the note's contents. There wasn't much to it, just a desire to go with the girl to the exclusion of all others.

'Well?' I asked after a decent interval.

'I won't go with him,' she announced, 'because he's too serious.' It was a fair assessment. He was a serious chap. He never laughed.

Too serious! Well it takes all kinds to make a world but I feel that we have too many serious people. Then it must be said that we are all either too fat or too lean, too tall or too small, too rich or too poor and so forth and so on.

'Let me have men about me who are fat,' says Julius Caesar, 'all lean men are dangerous.'

They may have been dangerous in Caesar's time but

fat men have been more dangerous since. Look, for instance, at Goering, Mussolini and Stalin and let us not forget Idi Amin, prime bucks all.

The apple of the agricultural worker's eye would not have known of these men. They had not come into prominence and anyway I doubt if she would follow their careers with any great degree of interest because everybody would agree at the time that she was very self-centred and had little interest in anything outside of herself.

I daresay that the opposite of seriousness would be cheerfulness. It is good to be cheerful but the phrase Cheerful Idiot was not coined by accident and onlookers could not be blamed if they deduced that a non-stop cheerful man had something the matter with him. The point I am trying to make here is that there is no real difference between a cheerful man and a serious man. All we have to go on is surface cheerfulness and surface seriousness. The girl who turned down our friend John Rest did not take this into account. Indeed most people don't and this is a pity because it means that serious-on-the surface contenders for the hands of non-discerning females are at a disadvantage.

Then there's the expression 'God loves a cheerful giver.' The truth is that God loves all kinds of givers and I believe that a cheerful giver suffers less when giving than does a serious giver. The cheerful giver gives instinctively and often starves his wife and family whereas the serious giver wrestles with his conscience a good deal before parting or not parting, as the case may be, with his few bob.

Those who teach Shakespeare have a lot to answer for.

For several days I had a low image of myself over what Caesar said about lean men. The teacher had agreed with Caesar but then one day as I was eating some boiled mutton and parsley sauce it dawned on me that the teacher in question was the fattest in the school. He would naturally agree with Caesar.

The girl who turned down John Rest did so for superficial reasons. I saw her several times. She had disimproved with age, she died lately, God rest her. I often meet John Rest and he said to me after he heard of her death 'I hope she don't be turned down by Saint Peter. He seems a serious man to me.'

Injured Impostors

WHEN I WAS A PRIME buck playing football one never took a dive when the brain was stunned and the physiognomy frequently altered by a belt of a fist from an impassioned opponent. One simply would not give it to say to the assailant or to the sideline in general that damage had been inflicted. One carried on and never resorted to the heinous ploy of feigning insensibility in the hope that the culprit might be sent to the line. More often than not the blows would be accidental or, at worst, delivered in the heat of the moment under extreme provocation.

One's pride was on the line and to find oneself in a horizontal position after a moderate straight left or half-hearted right cross was a sign of premature senility or naked pretence. Worse still one could be accused at the tender age of twenty of suffering from osteoporosis of the lower mandible or, as it is more succinctly referred to in pugilistic circles, a glass jaw. Nobody wanted the name of a glass jaw. The proprietor of such a handicap was as suspect as a cardboard crutch and could let you down when you need it most. In fact I have personally known cases where it grievously militated against the matrimonial prospects of otherwise acceptable young gentlemen. Their prospective fathers-in-law would flinch and shake their heads disapprovingly as though to say that the glass-jawed aspirant to their daughter's hand could not be depended upon as a supportive member of the family.

Suppose there was, for instance, a sideline fracas would not the owner of the glass jaw be the first to succumb to one of the wild blows for which such fracas are noted! Suppose again, for instance, a high ball came dropping into the square and, that in leaping for it, the glass-jawed man accidentally brushed against the elbow of the full-back, might not the day be lost and might not the progeny of the suitor in question be also possessed of the fatal flaw for which their father was sidelined!

Today, alas, there are players who will cheerfully take a dive after inconsequential contact with an innocent marker. Covering their faces with their hands they collapse with protracted groans in writhing heaps until the referee, if he is gullible enough, points the finger of dismissal to the sideline and stands imperiously with his hands behind his back, impervious to the pleas of an innocent Gael, another victim of ham-acting and gross deceit.

I have frequently pleaded with the producers of my plays to come with me to playing fields near and far where they might behold for themselves the disgraceful shenanigans of injured impostors who should be on the stages of our professional theatres. With consummate ease they are able to convince referees that they are on the very threshold of death and remember that none of these have ever trod the boards at even amateur level. There are also some magnificent performances to be seen on our television screens.

Fortunately most referees are not so easily duped and I recall a great story in which a known dissembler was knocked out twice in the same contest or so he would have the referee believe. When he fell to the ground for the second time clutching a nose which, to the inexperienced onlooker, must have been surely broken in several places the referee pulled him to his feet and shook him soundly, shouting at the same time into the blackguard's ear. 'If,' said the referee, 'you get knocked out a third time, I'll send you to the line.'

The timely ultimatum soon put an end to his posturings.

We had in this part of the world an elegant half-forward who could collapse like a punctured balloon when fairly beaten for a ball. It was said of him that he was responsible for the sending to the line of fourteen innocent men and I wonder if this constitutes a record!

I was once sent to the line for taking a back swing at a persistent jersey puller. I missed him by a foot but he fell to the ground all the same, a lifeless parody of a once-supple athlete. To give the referee his due he had some misgivings before pointing to the sideline. He never consulted the linesman for the good reason that linesmen in those days wisely kept their minds to themselves. They, after all, had to stand for an hour with their backs to the crowd whereas the referee could run all over the place and find himself out of harm's way. For a moment I thought I was merely to be cautioned but then a bystander, probably a brother who had been ministering to the stricken player, spoke as follows – 'he'll live all right,' he said sadly, 'but he'll do no good.' That was the second last time I was sent to the line. The last time was when I ran out of wind in my middle thirties and was summarily dismissed by my own mentors.

Cartoons

THE PROBLEM WITH LONG words, complicated words or words that don't sound the way they look, is that the user is frequently misunderstood. Only the other week I heard a dead man described as being very parsleymonious. This is fine for those who can put two and two together. For those who can't, life can be full of misunderstandings. There's nothing will get a man into deep water faster than mispronunciation. I know because I am a word experimenter. While I was serving my time at this dangerous trade I often put my foot in it but then that's the way with all apprentices or, as our ancestors used to say, you can't put an old head on young shoulders.

I had a man working for me once and he had a problem with words. I engaged him for a period of one month. His job was to whitewash the backyard and the outhouses, to sort out loose slates, to clean out the eaves' shoots and to replace pieces of plaster which had been evicted by those relentless intruders, wind and rain. One afternoon he came to me and announced that 'better than whitewash' would be needed for an outhouse door.

'Whitewash is all right,' he said, 'but it don't suit doors or windows.'

It transpired that there was a half tin of paint in the store-room 'but,' said he, 'it's as ould as Methusaleh and it will take a fair share of porpentine to thin it out.'

Porpentine! Porpentine!

Where had I heard that delightful word before. Surely

it enhanced the fringes of a poem or enriched a love-song. What he meant, of course, was turpentine but we both knew what he meant and that's all that really matters. It's not the way you say it. Rather is it the way you get it across.

That night as I sat drinking a pint of beer with a crony it all came back to me. Readers will recall that part of Hamlet where Hamlet himself is addressed by his father's ghost, as fine a piece of writing as ever was quilled by the great bard:

> I am thy father's spirit,
> Doom'd for a certain term to walk the night ...
> But that I am forbid
> To tell the secrets of my prison-house
> I could a tale unfold whose lightest word
> Would harrow up thy soul, freeze thy young blood,
> Make thy two eyes, like stars, start from their spheres,
> Thy knotted and combined locks to part
> Like quills upon the fretful porpentine.

So we see gentle reader that if you were to put a porpentine into a half tin of paint instead of turpentine there would be disastrous consequences. The moral is that we should ponder well before we deliver verbal broadsides which could provoke the same reaction as shrapnel.

I remember well to have been loitering in the vicinity of an ice-cream stand in Ballybunion many years ago. A small man, accompanied by a wife and five children, placed an order for seven cartoons of ice-cream.

'Cartoons!' the youngster behind the counter scoffed, 'go up town to the cinema and you'll get all the cartoons you want.'

The small man shot out a left fist. The youngster fell.

The small man moved with his party to the next stand and was accommodated without comment. If the small man had said carton instead of cartoon there would have been no trouble. If the youngster had used his imagination he wouldn't have been floored.

Spot On

THIS IS THE TALE OF side-tracking, of deflection, of deviation, all brought about by curiosity. All of fifty years ago my father, God be good to him, who was a teacher sent me downstairs to his study with instructions to look up a certain word in his Virtue's English dictionary. He was suffering at the time from influenza and maybe this was one of the reasons why the meaning of the word in question was not at once apparent to him. I told myself that it must be a difficult word indeed when a teacher could not understand it.

I set out at once and located the dictionary without bother. I thumbed easily through the pages until I came to P. Sure enough the word was there. It was propaedeutic. I smirked when I saw the meaning. It meant the preliminary learning connected with any art or science. I was about to close the dictionary and make my way upstairs to his bedroom when my attention was drawn to some strange-sounding words in the vicinity of the word which had baffled my father. There was, for instance, propendent and there was propolis and there was pronaos. I had never come across any of these before.

Although the dictionary was quite heavy and I was quite young I stayed in a standing position for what must have been the best part of an hour before returning the book to the shelf where it always held pride of place. By this time I had completely forgotten why I had been standing in the study in the first place.

I made my way out into the street where I encountered some other idlers who stood around aimlessly for the want of something better to do. Eventually we decided to go picking sloes, the time being mid-October and the day being fine. We did not return to our home until the pangs of hunger assailed us. After supper I called in to see my father. He seemed to be on the mend.

'Did you find out the meaning of the word?' he asked.

'What word?' I asked.

'Propaedeutics,' he returned.

I forgot,' I said.

'Serves me right,' he said, 'for sending you downstairs in the first place.'

I tried to look chastened.

'Don't worry,' he said, 'I discovered the meaning the moment you went outside the door but I was too weak to call you back. It has something to do with preliminary learning has it not?'

'That's right,' I recalled, 'but how did you find out?'

'I read and reread the sentence,' he explained, 'and returned to some of the preceding sentences for further elucidation and I had no problem. I did not even have to resort to my ailing Greek.'

'Why did you send me downstairs?' I asked.

'You looked like a prisoner,' he explained, 'so I gave you the excuse to escape.'

He told me that it was always possible to deduce the meaning of any word if one read the sentence carefully over and over and, failing that, to read the paragraph and failing that to read the page.

'Suppose you get the wrong meaning?' I suggested.

'Then I am not to blame,' he responded cheerfully, 'the writer is to blame. If the writer knows his job he will not befuddle the reader. If he uses the word out of context he is not a real writer but rather a shaper or a shower-offer.'

Since that far-off time I have found the old man's observation to be spot on, to be pukka, to be dinkum in fact.

RESOURCEFULNESS

THE FIRST TIME I was charged with being 'found on' a
licensed premises was in 1953 on the night of the Sunday
that Kerry beat Armagh in the all-Ireland football final. The
spot was Ballybunion where thousands of such breaches of
the law had already taken place over the famed resort's
colourful lifetime.

A group of us were happily seated in Mikey Joe's
American Bar when the imperious knock sounded on the
front door. In those days the first thing a publican did
when an arm of the law knocked upon his door was to go
at once to the back door to see if there was also a civic
guard on public house duty there. Alas there was and the
proprietor was obliged to admit the keepers of the peace
from both the back and front which amounted to being
surrounded on all sides since there were no side-doors on
the premises.

'Account for your presence,' a young guard asked as
he readied his pencil and notebook.

Like any law-abiding citizen I provided him with the
name and address of a brother who resided in Dublin. He
continued with his name-taking and it was then I beheld a
friend of mine who had been in our company all night as
he headed towards the door with a box of empty bottles.

'Scuse me!' he addressed himself imperiously to the
guard who moved out of his way, muttering an apology as
he did. It was a good ploy. My friend deposited the bottles
in the backyard and made good his escape through the

backway and onto the street where a large crowd had gathered.

Another companion of mine who had been the life and soul of our party till the knocking sounded was nowhere to be seen in the public house. Eventually when all the names had been taken I spotted him behind the counter with his coat off washing glasses. He had moved there the moment the guards appeared. As an apparent employee of the premises he would be exempt from having his name taken although there was no such law on the statutes at the time.

Another member of our party sought temporary refuge in the toilets when he beheld the uniforms. There with several others he stood vainly waiting in the hope that the guards would not venture into that hallowed place. The guards, however, although one of them was a mere rookie were well acquainted with all the tricks of would-be escapers. As soon as they indicated that they were about to enter the toilets my friend appeared with a coarse brush in his hand and motioning the rookie to one side intimated that he was sorry for what happened but that there were no hard feelings and would the guard like a drink on the house in atonement for what he was obliged to go through. Now who could blame the guard for believing that he was in the presence of the pub's proprietor. Who else would have the aplomb or the authority to offer him a drink on the house.

He declined the offer of the drink and instead accepted the pretender's handshake. The pretender stopped at the rear door which was under the younger guard's supervision.

'I'll close this if you have no objection,' he said to the guard. So saying he closed the door from the outside and made good his escape. A number of other pretenders were not so lucky. Upstairs a man washing his feet in a basin of water was not taken for a member of the household as he hoped and another who slipped into bed in the nude was forced to evacuate and dress. Still by resourcefulness and cockiness were the scales of justice balanced as it were.

A Bull in August

This morning I met a sourpuss. I hadn't encountered one in years for the good reason that most of my outings are to places where humans are few and far between. I meet animal sourpusses often enough especially in the late summer. These in the main would be bulls who have been stretched to their sexual limits by the demands of numerous cows and heifers. These animal sourpusses need to be kept at a distance because your sourpuss bull will attack without provocation venting his wrath on luckless humans and turning his ponderous posterior to the cows and heifers who left him in such a state of debilitation.

The sourpuss I met this morning was male and in his forties. He scowled, growled and cleared the street in front of him like a tank.

'Watch where you're going!' I heard an old lady say. For a moment I thought he was going to demolish her. I passed him the time of day in cheerful tones but all I received in return was an almighty snort.

'Wrong side of the bed,' the old lady ventured as soon as he was out of earshot.

He entered a supermarket and emerged after a few moments followed by a blonde woman who looked to be half his years. He seemed to be upbraiding her but, to give her no more than her due, she gave as good as she got and went back in.

'That's the second wife,' the old lady, 'he bullied the first one into her grave and she a great woman entirely that went nowhere, not even the bingo.'

Our fiend was now returning the way he had come. I thought for an awful moment that he was about to bellow before charging. I decided that it might be prudent not to salute him on this occasion. It was he who took it upon himself to address myself and the old lady.

'What are ye f ... looking at?' he asked belligerently.

'Nothing,' the old lady answered at which he bridled and bristled and barked like a mastiff. He decided not to devour us there and then. Instead he turned on his heel and proceeded to his car. He sat there glumly awaiting the blonde woman who was still in the supermarket.

Eventually she appeared in the doorway and made her way to the car where he still fumed and frothed and manufactured four-letter foulies. His new wife was followed by a supermarket attendant who bore her bags of groceries in her wake. She opened the boot of the car and he deposited the groceries therein. She entered the car but so vehement was the tirade of abuse which greeted her that she re-emerged at once banging the door behind her.

'Ah sure I have it all now,' said the old lady. I waited for elaboration as she folded her arms and nodded her head.

'The young wan is too much for him. She has the taspy knocked out of him and he's fit for nothing only mischief – the same as a bull in August.'

There it all was. The answer was provided by a gentle old lady who knew the ways of men and bulls. I was tempted at the outset to call this contribution 'Of Bulls and

Men' but that might give the game away prematurely.

I resolved there and then to make allowance for all the grumpy, middle-aged men I would be likely to meet thereafter, especially those who might be married to young, demanding spouses.

PROPHET NEVER AT A LOSS

CALLAGHAN THE PROPHET, AS his neighbours called him, lived only a few miles outside my native town. He was a man of few words and these were almost always apocalyptical. I remember one morning, as he took the wrapping from a string of sausages, he was instructed by his wife to snip the sausages apart with the bodkin which she extended to him.

'Woman,' Callaghan solemnly, 'know you not that what God had joined together no man dare sunder?'

'Yes,' said Callaghan's spouse, 'but not sausages.'

'Know you not,' said Callaghan, 'that she who liveth by the sword shall perish by the sword?'

When both had breakfasted the wife addressed herself to the Prophet.

'Go out now,' said she, 'and dig the drills for the potatoes.'

'Lo and behold,' said Callaghan, 'he who diggeth the pits shall perish therein.'

'But,' said his beloved, 'if we have no potatoes we'll have no dinner.'

'Better,' said Callaghan, 'a dinner of herbs where love is than a stalled ox and hatred therewith.'

'I'll report you to my brother,' the wife warned. Indeed the brother in question and Callaghan were often at loggerheads.

'You do just that,' said Callaghan, raising his eyes aloft

to the heavens, 'and I maketh him to lie down among green pastures.'

That night Callaghan arrived home from my native town in a drunken state. He had fallen by chance upon some wedding guests. The wife called him every evil name under the sun and threatened to leave right away for her brother's house.

'The Lord shall bless and keep thee,' said Callaghan, quoting from Numbers, vi. 24. 'The Lord maketh his face shine upon thee and be gracious unto thee. The Lord lifteth up his countenance upon thee and give thee peace.'

At that moment the moon broke free from its jailers, the clouds, and lighted up Callaghan's features through the panes of the kitchen window. He took off his clothes and allowed the moonlight to bathe his body. He raised his bony arms aloft and spoke to the ceiling overhead. 'Naked came I out of my mother's womb and naked shall I return thither. The Lord giveth and the Lord taketh away. Blessed be the name of the Lord.'

In the bed his spouse turned her back on him. A feigned snore indicated her boredom.

Callaghan began to wail toward the still unclouded moon. 'My days are swifter than a weaver's shuttle,' he cried, 'and are spent without hope.'

The wife sighed by his side.

'Ere the cock shall crow three times,' Callaghan called out aloud, 'thou shalt kiss me three times in the moonlight for so it hath been ordained.'

And so it came to pass and later, as the clouds returned

to the darkening skies, Callaghan slept the sleep of the just. When morning came the stars dimmed their lights and made their silent goodbyes to the heavens. The dawn rose in the east and the light of day touched the pair in the bed.

'Let there be light!' Callaghan shouted.

'What's up?' his wife asked in alarm.

'Your eggs!' Callaghan reminded her. 'What way do you want them boiled?'

The Time I Was Dead

I DON'T BELIEVE I ever told you about the time I was dead. Despite this I have never felt more alive than I do at this moment. In fact the captious old midwife who brought me into the world informed my father that I would live to be a great age if intoxicating drink didn't get the better of me prematurely. In this respect it has been touch and go for many a long day now. You might say that drinkwise I'm just ahead of the posse. The bother is that this particular posse catches up with everybody sooner or later regardless of whether one drinks or drinks not.

One balmy evening recently after returning from a stroll by the river I sat myself down on my favourite stool in my favourite bar which is my own and treated myself to a pint of beer. As I sat imbibing at my leisure a good-looking girl, from Mayo it transpired later, sat down beside me. She noticed a painting of me on the wall behind the counter.

'Is he long dead?' she asked the barmaid.

'He's dead a nice while now,' the barmaid answered, 'although you couldn't trust him. He could reappear at any moment.'

The visitor swallowed a little from her lager and addressed herself to me. 'What got him in the end?' she asked-ed.

'I wish I knew,' I told her truthfully, adding to myself that it was just as well I could not forecast what I might eventually expire from although if it wasn't one thing it would most certainly be another.

A week passed and a busload of German tourists arrived. I was seated on my favourite stool only this time I was drinking whiskey. The Germans too believed me to be dead. Even the courier who was Irish said a prayer for me when he was confronted with my painting.

'God he was an ugly-looking customer,' said the courier.

'Lak a vervulf,' said a German female.

'Nein. Nein,' said another, 'more lak a wampire.'

'What did he die of?' the courier asked the barmaid.

'Thirst,' she answered.

'Thirst!' everybody echoed incredulously.

'How could he die of thirst in the middle of a bar?' the courier asked.

'He was too drunk to come downstairs,' the barmaid explained.

This seemed to satisfy courier and Germans alike.

'There is wuss ways off goingk,' an elderly German gentleman announced and he called for a whiskey.

No week passes but somebody asks how long I've been dead or what did I die from. The barmaid always dispenses the same answer. Those present who know I'm alive keep their mouths shut. It all began after I underwent major surgery. Some reports said I was dead, others alive. I suppose the best description of me at the present time is to say that I am dead and alive.

The question arises as to whether I am worth more dead than alive. That, of course, will not be resolved in this place or at this time but I will be spoken of highly because it is the fashion never to say a bad word about the dead in this part of the world.

I must be the only man around who knows how Lazarus felt when he was raised from the dead because I have been consigned to the dead and I have risen. I rose yesterday morning at twenty past nine, was pronounced dead at half past twelve and rose again on a barstool at quarter to ten that night.

Pubology

Since I spoke recently on public houses and the wisdom to be found therein I have received numerous letters of congratulations for highlighting these hitherto undisclosed aspects of pubology. One letter deserves my immediate attention however. It comes from a city reader who says that he has been in our pub here in Listowel several times but he has never seen me. That is quite possible since I cannot spend all my time in the pub. However it could also be that he is looking in the wrong direction for, as well as looking for me inside the counter, he should look for me outside the counter. The latter is my stamping ground during my hours of recreation. Here I may be seen with glass in hand at the drinking hour of evening.

The other letters offer contributions drawn from their own experiences of pub life. A woman from Drumcollogher who supplies her name and address and who used to work in a pub one time recalls a customer who slipped his domestic moorings whenever he sighted visitors in the vicinity of his home.

'He was what you might call a philosopher,' the Drumcollogher woman remembers. 'He had one saying for which I will personally remember him – "For the protection of its inmates, if nothing else, every house should have its visiting hours".'

I couldn't agree more. For some reason totally beyond my ken whenever I sit down to a meal I am besieged by visitors. The phone-caller too always rings at meal-times for he knows you must eat and are likely to be seated at your own table when he lifts the phone to harass you.

I mentioned cures when talking about pub lore. On Sunday night last as we were about to close for the night a farmer from an outlying townland arrived offering as an excuse for his lateness the fact that he was a martyr to arthritis. While he sipped his whiskey he was offered several cures. One man in particular had a most unusual remedy. To cure his own arthritis he regularly singes his bare bottom with burning newspapers as they once did to clear recalcitrant feathers from the carcasses of hastily plucked geese. The treatment, if it left a few blisters itself, always worked. I mean where else would you hear it but in a public house. I have heard of cures that would make the hair stand on your head. Now there's a real cure especially if your head is bare.

I often wonder why nobody has written a book about pub lore or pub sayings or pub medicine. Could be, as the old saying would have us believe, that the jokes of the night before are not nearly so funny in the morning. I was often tempted to write a book about my experiences in the pub trade and nothing else but I never got around to doing it. Maybe I'm doing it now through this medium.

I once had a customer who consumed all his meals early in the day ending with his dinner which he devoured at three o'clock in the afternoon so that he could go to pub early and remain there until closing time. He lived a happy life. So did his wife who, as long as she was permitted to indulge in bingo every night of the week, never objected to his drinking habits. She managed their pensions. She presented him with the price of two pints each afternoon before his departure and with his natural charm, guile and cunning he always managed to have rounds stood to him by those he praised for their courage and generosity. Pubs are filled with men who need recognition for unexposed talents.

Pubs and poets go together and one of the better verses I have heard over the years was composed by a drunken man after he had been introduced to a female from the townland of Ballybrohawlinam.

'Where in God's name,' said he, 'is Ballybrohawlinam?'

'Spell it,' called an onlooker.

'No,' said a third, 'get something to rhyme with it.'

The drunken man provided the following without a moment's hesitation:

> Beautiful are the bottoms of the women of Ballybrohawlinam
> With their chaste eyes heavenwards as though they'd no
> bottoms at all on 'em.

JUST RISEN

THE MOST DANGEROUS TYPE of visitor is he who when invited to partake of a cup of tea informs his host that he must decline because he has only just risen from the table. Very good if he presents this fable at a time other than mealtimes but if he arrives while a meal is in progress and the offer is repeated he will eat his unfortunate host out of house and home. At least this has always been our experience with the man who has 'only just risen from the table'. To be fair to him he has, more or less, laid his cards on the table which he now faces.

Watch out therefore for all those who say that they have only just risen. What he is really saying is this: 'I am after rising from one table but this should not preclude me from sitting at another.' Most sinister of all visitors is he who sits himself down and waits to be asked if he will partake of a cup of tea or a bite to eat but who, when accepting the offer, does so conditionally. 'I am most grateful,' he is sure to say, 'but I won't have it unless you are all having it.'

The implication here is that he does not consider himself a worthy enough guest to merit a meal or even a snack on his own unless there is already a household meal in the offing as a matter of course. This is what he would like to infer but very often his qualified acceptance becomes garbled in transit like so many other messages and is quite often taken to mean this: 'I will accept your kind offer to dine but only if everybody else is dining as well.'

This display of magnanimity endears him to all present especially those who are not members of the house-hold and who would eat any given amount of food at any given time provided they didn't have to pay for it. They were prepared to applaud the invitation and why shouldn't they! Were it not for the conditional clause contained in the acceptance by the visitor they would never have been in-vited to eat in the first place. Was it not logical then that they should give their thanks to the visitor rather than the householder!

There were many households where, because of abuses of the aforementioned nature, the householders were re-luctant to be expansive when offering refreshment to visit-ors. 'Sure you won't have tea!' was a common safeguard employed by those who had been bitten too often in the past. What this meant was that the householder was more than willing to lay the table for the tea but the visitor had given the distinct impression that he was already over-fed and in no immediate need of tea. 'Sure you won't have tea!' could also mean 'surely you won't have tea!'

Another suitable ploy is to stir up the fire or plug in the kettle until this venerable vessel starts to sing. This should provoke the visitor into posing the following question: 'I hope you're not boiling that kettle for me?' Thus a tea-making situation with all its implications is averted be-cause the visitor has implied that he does not mind seeing the kettle come to the boil so long as it is not being boiled especially for him. He may, of course, if pressed allow the kettle to be boiled for him but the tendency in this less hospitable day and age is not to provide tea and all that goes with it unless it is asked for specifically.

There was a time in this much-abused land when there would be a mad rush to rinse out the teapot the moment a visitor was reported to be approaching the house. I hope our findings on this occasion will be of some assistance to those who have suffered more than their share from voracious visitors who depend largely on excursions to liberal households for their daily bread.

ECONOMICS

I HAVE ENDEAVOURED ALL of my life to be more economical with the use of words and whenever I can I delete unnecessary extras from my scripts and what-have-you. There are times when, because of demands, one is obliged to go on but largely speaking I strive to be brief and eschew trimmings.

While I love the colourful sentence and the flowing paragraph there is always at the back of my mind the desire to cut it short and proceed with the business in hand. That is why I hold certain writers, many of them anonymous, in high regard and that is why I open the proceedings here today with a comment from that late and great travelling man Jack Faulkner sometimes of Glin and more times of Listowel.

I was seated behind the counter reading an epic poem while Jack who was then in his heyday sat on the other side nursing a pint of stout.

'What's that you're reading?' Jack asked after a while.

'An epic poem,' I replied.

'What sort of a poem is that?' Jack asked.

'It's a long poem,' I explained.

'Poetry,' said Jack after a pause, 'is bad enough without it being long.'

Now there is a truly economical statement and it came from a gentleman whose proud boast it was that he had no education.

'I'd sooner a tomb nor a school,' Jack said once as we

conversed about the vagaries of life and the relationship between education and survival.

'Say that verse about the pheasant,' Jack had insisted at the time. I obliged.

> And will Euclid teach me how to light a fire
> Of green twigs in the rain
> Or how to twist a pheasant's neck
> So he won't screech out in pain.

'The man that wrote that,' said Jack, 'was a wise man. Who's that he was again?'

'Clifford from Cahersiveen,' I told him. 'Sigerson Clifford.'

'Brevity is the soul of wit!' said Shakespeare, 'and tediousness but the limbs and outward flourishes.'

Of limbs and flourishes I have had my fill. Give me brevity any day, rare and sweet virtue that never bores.

My granddaughter and myself have a common poem which she admires as much as I do. It's an epitaph as well and epitaphs for the most part because of sound financial reasons are the essence of brevity. Here is the piece:

> Here lie the bones of Pecos Bill.
> He always lied and always will.
> He once lied loud.
> He now lies still.

Could you beat that and probably composed by a barfly without the advantage of schooling. My other favourite is an equally anonymous effort about a sheep-stealer by the name of Thomas Kemp who was hanged:

> Here lie the bones of Thomas Kemp
> Who lived by wool and died by hemp.

Now that's what I call economy, rich and rare and always repeatable. Then there's the modesty of the man who composed it. He writes a masterpiece and is too humble to write his name. There's a friend of mine a poet, one Michael Hartnett who told me that he once addressed a mirror one night in a hotel and asked:

> Mirror, mirror on the wall!
> Who is the briefest of us all?

What answer came back? Why cuckoo of course, just cuckoo and why not. In two notes that dusky ambassador from Morocco tells us that summer is at hand. Now that's economy.

HOLY WATER FONTS

ONE OF THE STRANGEST sights I ever saw was a black ass drinking from a holy water font outside a church in my native town. Sated and sanctified the creature turned slowly and hobbled off about his business which was the everlasting search for grass. This was many years ago when I was a young man who was often possessed of an unquenchable thirst for knowledge. It is a thirst which only comes after one has left school.

'Did you see that!' an elderly nun addressed me as she pointed a finger in the direction of the departing donkey.

I told her I did and for the sake of conversation remarked that it was an extraordinary business entirely.

'There's no one more entitled to it,' she said wistfully, 'we should never begrudge an ass.'

The same woman told me that poetry was your only man, that other writing was only the watering down of the essence which was poetry.

The only other creature I saw drinking from an outdoor holy water font was a sparrow. The font was full; otherwise the tiny fledgling wouldn't have been able to partake. It isn't that birds or donkeys have a preference for holy water over other waters. It's simply a matter of availability.

I was once intrigued in Ballybunion during my green years. I beheld a small man in his middle years with his arm around a very large and very round woman some years his junior. As they left the church he dipped his finger in the font and blessed his companion but never blessed himself. I looked in the font thinking there might have been only sufficient water for the blessing of one brow but no, the font was half full. I discovered subsequently from our family doctor that there were people who would not bless their brows with holy water lest they 'pick up something out of it' – his words. He told me of others who would not touch holy water because it might burn them. These would have been people whose consciences were troubling them. Many people drank holy water as a cure for what ailed them especially Knock water and Lourdes water. A relation of my own claimed it made her drunk.

The reason I bring up holy water fonts is because they seem to be disappearing from the scene. In my childhood no house was without a holy water font. It was always placed near the door so that incomings and outgoings might dip their fingers and bless themselves. I remember Brendan Behan was once leaving our kitchen when he paused to bless himself and afterwards he praised my wife for the quality of the font which was made in Beleek. On his way out he sang:

> The winds that blow from Gardiner Street to Kimmage
> Are perfumed by the knackers as they blow
> And the women on the tip head picking cinders
> Speak a language that the clergy do not know

The next time he called he enquired after the holy water font and blessed himself from it before he left. Earlier he had stopped with his friend Sean O'Shea at Jimmy Joy's pub in Abbeyfeale. O'Shea had refused to stop earlier.

Brendan leapt from the car and knelt on the ground looking up at James J. Joy's name with outstretched hands.

'Oh James Jesus Joy I adore you,' he cried out before going in for a drink.

But where have all the holy water fonts gone! We live in a world of unblessed brows, of wrinkling nose bridges, of unholy hair lines. In my youth a house without a holy water font was like a drake without feathers, a watercourse without a stream, a cow without an udder, a face without a nose. Give us back our holy water fonts before its too late.

I've spent the last hour trying to remember the final verse of the Kimmage song Brendan used to sing and I think I may have it at last:

> Some day I'll go back again to Kimmage
> Be it only at the closing of my mind
> To see the little children beat their grannies
> Or tripping up the crippled and the blind.

THE LAST SHALL BE FIRST

THE FIRST SHALL BE last and the last shall be first. So says the Good Book. There are also numerous references to Pharisees, Publicans and the likes who occupy front seats in places of worship and there are mentions, all derogatory, of those who would assume predominance or prominence at feasts and celebrations. All very fine but who are we going to put in the front seats and the head of the table? Recently at a public meeting the first four rows were totally empty whereas the back rows were crowded.

A few Sundays ago at church I was witness to the same thing except that on this occasion it was acutely uncomfortable. There we were, the missus and I, seated happily, having moved on to the very inside of our pew like we were supposed to do when suddenly the pew was invaded by a family of several who packed it to suffocation. We were crammed like the proverbial sardines but worse was to follow. A large woman followed by a smaller family of only three also decided that the already over-crowded pew was the place for them.

The missus and I removed ourselves to a pew where there was plenty of room although after awhile this filled up too although not to capacity. The tragedy was that there were several empty seats at the front of the church. The massgoers, however, avoided these as though they were the very hobs of hell.

It would seem then that church authorities have hoisted themselves on their own petards. On the one hand it is suggested that we should avoid the front pews like the plague because only Publicans and Pharisees aspire to such exalted places. On the other hand I have heard clergymen and chairmen and committee members urging people to avail themselves of front seats. What is the poor punter to do!

Is this reluctance to avail of front seats really the fault of the church or is it just downright perverseness on the part of the plain people of our parishes up and down the country! The front pew is the last place they want to be seen.

The other night in the bar a man insisted that the front pews should be removed. 'But,' said another, 'the second seat will then be the front seat and we will be no nearer a solution.' 'And,' said another again, 'if you remove the second seat the third seat will be the first seat and so forth and so on *ad infinitum.*' We were now bordering on the apocalyptical which is no place for a semi-drunken group of laymen to be.

The last shall be first and the first shall be last! I saw the epigram being enacted many years ago as I was leaving the great island of pilgrimage, Lough Derg, of a Sunday morning. The longboats were drawn up to take us away and Monsignor Flood who was in charge of that place at that time urged us all beforehand to proceed in an orderly and a Christian fashion to the boats and to take others especially the feeble and the aged into account. His words fell on deaf ears because there was an immediate rush to the boats by a crowd of recently-shriven delinquents who should have known better after their penitential sojourn in that holy place.

'The last shall be first,' said the good Monsignor and so saying he ordered the leaders to make a turn away from the shore. They did so reluctantly and we who were last were first. I wasn't at all sure it was where I wanted to be but I appreciated Monsignor Flood's point and he was a straight and a good man if ever there was one.

As Tom Somers said when he approached the line after being lapped in the five thousand metres, 'Here I am, first at last what was always behind before.'

FANTAIL

I HAD A FEMALE cousin who could easily be mistaken in the distance for a fantail pigeon. She was also a cooer and as soon as she drew near she cooed. She walked exactly like a pigeon and she cooed like a pigeon although she could not and would not fly. She was at her pigeonly best during family rows when with gentle but sustained cooing she would calm everybody down until harmony reigned. Then she would coo a little to herself and strut elegantly homewards.

The reason I resurrect her is because I could have used her the other night. At the front of these here licensed premises a family from the hinterland were on the verge of dismembering each other. Then a woman who looked exactly like my cousin erupted from a nearby motor car and strutted towards the most vocal and truculent of those who were gathered close by. She hauled back and let go with her handbag. Contact was made and the offending buck was felled without as much as a murmur. I was shocked for I had foolishly believed that she would behave like my female cousin and commence cooing as a matter of course.

The blow with the handbag, a deadly weapon surely in the hands of a mature female, drew a violent reaction from a younger member of the family. She struck the woman who had delivered the blow with her own handbag, a considerably smaller one and I am glad to say that it had no effect whatsoever. Suddenly everybody was involved and many wild blows were drawn. Thankfully, because of the advanced inebriation of the warring factions few blows reached their destination. A passing gentleman, elderly and serene, stopped to chat and we watched as the family fought tooth and nail, the woman who resembled the fantail pigeon fighting and shouting more viciously and more loudly than anybody.

'What a change,' I said to the new arrival, 'from old Maggie Monty!' and I pointed a finger at Maggie's double who now held another woman firmly by the hair of the head with a view to bringing her to the ground where she might all the more easily maim her.

'Ah yes!' my elderly friend recalled fondly, 'poor Maggie that stopped more fights than the League of Nations and the United Nations put together.'

'And this virago looks so much like her,' I reminded him.

'But will not coo,' he said.

'But will not coo,' we both said together.

Indeed she looked at that moment as if she had never cooed in her life, that she had from the moment she was able to walk assumed a fighting stance and never resorted to peaceful means in order to resolve a problem.

'What has happened to the world at all!' I asked.

'Vodka,' he replied at once.

'Vodka!' I repeated the word.

'Vodka,' he confirmed, 'and if not vodka then surely gin. Indeed,' he continued indicating the fighting fantail, 'it would not surprise me if I was told that she had a bottle of

94

either drank for I have seen her in action and she would drink you and I under the table.'

We shook our heads at the folly of it all. What would have been once unthinkable was now commonplace. There was no vodka when I was a boy and we shall never know whether this was a good or a bad thing. It seems a pity however that there are no more cooers of the quality of Maggie Monty. We can put this down in part to vodka or to gin or to whiskey or whatever. In fact there are fewer peacemakers than ever before and isn't it well known that if Maggie Monty started a coo or two in this day and age she wouldn't be left with a feather in her fantail.

Piped Out

SOME YEARS AGO AT the final of a district league game I chanced to be safely surrounded by hundreds of partisan supporters in the stand. It was a close game and at half time I decided to abandon my position and come closer to the pitch which was shut off from the spectators by some wire mesh.

I don't know exactly what it was that drew me downward from the stand but I believe now as I did then that it was a simple, basic premonition that a row was in the offing. Inside the wire, separated from the crowd, were the mentors and selectors of both teams plus the usual supplement of unauthorised blackguards who find their way into such gatherings in the hope that mayhem will develop.

Just then I noticed a strange apparition. He was a spare, lean, almost emaciated little man. I might have missed him but for the fact that he had a pipe in his mouth. He seemed inoffensive enough although he clapped and shouted whenever his team registered a score. I thought it a strange thing that a man should carry a lighted pipe in his mouth in such surroundings.

Already there were rumblings in the sideline as the tempo of the encounter picked up with about fifteen minutes to go. Thugs began to shoulder each other and noisy threats were exchanged. Blows seemed imminent. I called the man with the pipe in his mouth and respectfully suggested to him that he take it from between his teeth without further delay 'because,' I said, 'this is no place for a man with a pipe in his mouth and when the fists fly you'll be the first to be at the receiving end.'

He answered by addressing me with a four letter word which was followed by the word 'off.'

I was astounded. There I was trying to save the fellow's life as it were and that's the thanks I got. I withdrew a few paces from the wire knowing full well that a wire, any wire is not proof against a stampede of enraged partisans.

Suddenly there was a loud cry from the majority present when the referee imperiously raised his hand and pointed it towards the sideline at the same time intimating to the offending player that he should proceed in the direction indicated. When the lawbreaker failed to obey the referee's instructions a full-scale fist fight broke out among the sideline supporters. Mayhem ensued but because of the ferocity of the fight it was of short duration. There were several casualties. There was one in particular who had his hands over his bloodied nose as he limped in the general direction of the sideline exit. He was, of course, the man who had been smoking the pipe. His knees gave way under him as he arrived at the gate which leads from the pitch to the pathway outside. I went to his assistance at once and gently deposited him in a comfortable public house convenient to the field which we had just vacated.

I called for a brandy for the wounded man and a pint of stout for myself. No sooner had he consumed the brandy than his speech returned. It was broken and it was slurred and it was tearful but I had no trouble understanding him.

'How did you know I was going to be struck down?' he asked.

'Simplicity itself,' I replied, 'you are a small slight man of advanced years, ideal fodder for a rampaging thug but your plight was compounded by the fact that you carried a smoking pipe in your gob. A man with a pipe in his mouth where there's a row in progress is just asking to have his nose or jaw broken.'

'My nose,' he confirmed between tears.

'A small, slight man with a pipe in his mouth,' I explained, 'is the epitome of provocation. After all,' I continued, 'why risk striking another thug and the prospect of retaliation when you see before you a ready-made victim with a pipe in his mouth.'

HORSEY-HORSEY

DAN PADDY ANDY THE great Irish matchmaker built two dance halls, one at Fahaduv and the other at his native Renagown. They were built as much for his own amusement as for the rustic patrons who came flocking there and who had, until Dan's enterprise surfaced, been completely at sea in the more sophisticated ballrooms of Listowel, Abbeyfeale, Tralee and Castleisland. The Renagown dance hall is now but a memory and, in fact, there is no trace to remind the passer-by of the great times enjoyed there in the 1940s and 1950s.

There was one great occasion when Dan Paddy Andy made a memorable speech after it was brought to his attention that certain ladies from surrounding towns were misbehaving after leaving the hall. It was the night of Easter Sunday some time in the mid 1940s. 'It has come to my attention,' said Dan, 'that townie pullets are laying out. If their wings get clipped me nor mine will not be accountable.'

As much as Dan disapproved of townie pullets he disapproved of Pounders even more. Pounders were young gentlemen who stamped violently on the wooden floor during reels and sets. In those days low shoes were worn by few and strong boots often hobnailed were the order of the night. Consequently there was a printed notice glued to the wall immediately inside the door. All it said was 'NO POUNDING'.

There was one particular tune which was anathema to

Dan Paddy Andy and that was 'Horsey, Horsey don't you stop'.

According to Tom Doran who is still hale and hearty and who, with his accordion, was the resident orchestra in the Renagown hall for many years, the opening bars of this tune were the signal for deafening pounding on the already treacherous floorboards. Some young bucks came to the hall for no purpose other than pounding and Horsey, Horsey was a heaven-sent opportunity. The minute Dan heard the first thunder of boots he called a halt to the music and climbed on to a wooden butter box kept specially in reserve for such purposes.

'If you have that much regard for Horsey, Horsey,' Dan told his listeners, 'you can have it all the way home on a road without boards to it.'

The same 'Horsey, Horsey' was responsible for a minor calamity in the late 1940s. There was a capacity crowd in the Renagown hall and all seemed to be going well. Dan decided to clear his lungs so he took a walk into the night air. On his way back he heard the pounding. The first thing he did was to stop the music upon entering the hall. When the music stopped so did the dancers. The cause of the commotion was a pair of Bogadawns. Bogadawn was the name given locally to big, soft, backward farmers' boys who wore boots as a rule but especially at dances.

Bogadawns at the time were notoriously wayward. Dan was therefore obliged to knock their heads together as was his wont when dealing with those who flouted his rules. This stopped their bucklepping quickly enough and served as a warning to other Bogadawns. Later these same Bogadawns would be tamed on the building sites of England by long hours and ruthless exploiters. When the two Bogadawns had departed Dan stood atop his butter box and made one of his famous announcements.

'Let it be known,' said Dan, 'that there is to be no more of this business known as Horsey, Horsy. Anyone I catch at it from this night forth will be banned from this hall for the remainder of their natural lives and moreover I will leave their rear ends in such a state that they won't be able to sit down for three years.'

That ended the Horsey, Horsey for once and for all.

My Club

I RECEIVED A QUESTIONNAIRE recently which, among other things, invited me to provide details of club membership.

Alas, at the moment, I am not a member of any club except of course the great club of humanity of which we are all members. Common as it is there are many incidental expenses and there is the ultimate fee which is the inevitable demise of the member regardless of his or her station. Naturally there are those who did not think it exclusive enough to they went and they begat their own clubs and kept themselves to themselves.

The first club of which I was a member through no achievement of my own was the AOHN. No, it's not the Ancient Order of Hibernians. It's far, far older. It was the Ancient Order of Have-Nots and its ranks are being swelled daily without ever advertising for membership. Nobody ever applied for membership of this particular club. You are born into it or you are not.

You cannot resign from the AOHN unless your luck changes and your circumstances improve through good luck or hard work. The latter, by the way, is never a guarantee because there are the powerful few who avail of the hard work of others to advance their own interests.

The second club of which I was a member was the IBNA. When I worked in England I led a careful, colourless life for the first weeks and then I fell among some Irish navvies who accepted me for membership of their club. There were certain qualifications. You needed to be beaten up by your own kind at least once and you needed to be able to go on long, foodless boozes until you puked your guts out. At the end of the initiation you were granted membership of the IBNA which simply means the Irish Buck Navvies Association. I am still an honorary member and although there are many who do not approve of the rules or the aims of the association the IBNA is not the worst club in the world and it has some mighty interesting members.

It is never easy to find acceptance by the IBNA. A preliminary degree such as the BL is a great help although not always a guarantee of membership. No it's not Bachelor of Law. It's Builder's Labourer and you can sit the examination in any recognised building site. When you have accumulated your builder's blisters you have your parchment so to speak.

To tell the truth I have been invited to join a club or two in my time but they all seemed to lack the folksy conviviality of the Irish Buck Navvies Association which may be lacking in *savoir-faire* according to some critics but is more than compensated by an immense *gaité de coeur* as every hoeur from one end of this country to the other knows well.

My own personal opinion about clubs who invite me to be a member is that they haven't found out about me yet so I better not accept in case they do. Of course every public house is a club with its own rules, with its members and occasional members. Break the rules and you're barred as with all clubs.

Then there's that great telegram attributed to Groucho Marx: 'Please accept my resignation. I don't want to belong to any club that will accept me as a member.'

Some people are not cut out for clubs whereas others belong in the same way that a fish belongs in a pond. Some have the same effect on clubs that a dark cloud has on the horizon and don't know a moment's happiness until they are kicked out. It's a great honour to be booted out of an exclusive club. Men go on to boast about it to their grand-children. Then there are those members who wait in vain for clubs to adopt them. They forget that when you can't find a club to suit you it becomes necessary to found your own.

UNDER THE BED

'WHERE WERE YE WHEN this man was under the bed?' The question was posed one heady night in Listowel while all around lighted sods impregnated with paraffin blazed on pitchforks and men with glazed eyes sought to dismember each other for no other reason than that they had different politics. You've guessed it! Dev was in town and while he wasn't the man in question, the man about whom the question was posed was, nevertheless, a significant figure in local politics. He hadn't died for his country or anything like that but he had kept his head and remained under the bed even when all seemed lost. At first the listeners were baffled by the question but he repeated it defiantly. 'Where were ye?' he demanded at the top of his voice, 'when this man was under the bed?'

'There aren't that many beds in Listowel' a wag shouted from the edge of the crowd.

What I'm trying to do here is defend those who hid under the bed when there were murderous gunmen abroad. It was at least better than leaving the country and if one was shot itself, they would have to find him first and will you tell me what sort of blackguard would pull a man from under a bed with a sick child and a nursing mother inside in it?

What went wrong with this country after the War of Independence was that there was no society for men who had been under the bed. Remember that those who had been under significantly outnumbered those who hadn't. I make out that for every hundred men who went under the bed only twelve did not. At least those are the figures we arrived at here in the pub the other night and many of those present were not a bit ashamed to admit that they were sired, even legally sired, by men who had been under the bed.

We all hid under the bed as children and what could be more natural than that we should return to the scenes of our childhood at the first sign of trouble. I mean where else would a man with no courage or a powerful instinct for preservation go unless it was under a bed. If we have had ancestors who hid under beds we should not be ashamed of it. At least they didn't turn their coats which is regarded as the most heinous sin of all on the Irish political front. Some day I will be passing through a graveyard and I hope I will see what I always wanted to see – that is a Celtic cross dedicated to the memory of the UBS.

UBS simply means Under-the-Bed-Society and I know of no man in this country who was fully compensated for being under his or any other bed. I have always regarded those who were under the bed as a sort of back-up, a last reserve who would emerge when all fruit failed, when their country needed them most. They were never given a chance and have been relegated to a lousy role in history by begrudgers who had no beds to go under.

Imagine what these men went through as they waited to be discovered by their would-be executioners! They must surely have died a thousand times before they were dragged out and even then they were treated disgracefully because no self-respecting soldier would shoot a man founder under a bed. It was beneath them. It was work for Black and Tans. I'll put this question to the begrudgers and vilifiers who would belittle those who went under the bed: Did you ever try to eat a four-course dinner while under a bed? Of course you didn't. You left that to men of sterner mettle who were used to four-course dinners, who always had enough to eat before the Johnny-Jump-Ups arrived on the scene.

Those of you whose fathers were under the bed have a perfect right to ask the question of begrudgers and others – 'Where were ye when our fathers were under the bed?'

TUGGERS AND PULLERS

WHEN I WAS YOUNGER we were led to believe that if a man was out late at night he was sure to have the tail of his coat pulled as he passed certain places such as the sites of fairy raths or graveyards or chilling places where men were said to have been murdered. Indeed I met a missioner once who claimed that it was not outside the realms of possibility 'but only,' said he, 'in cases where there was fornication involved.'

It never occurred to me at the time to ask him if the pursuit of murder, mayhem and robbery were exempt. One never questioned one's elders when I was a boy especially if they wore Roman collars. I would not have raised this question of coat-pulling at all but for the fact that I had the tail-end of my own tugged forcefully the other day. Notice I did not say pulled. I said tugged. I was in a long queue of mourners outside a funeral parlour in the district. When my turn came to enter the parlour so that I could pay my respects I found my coat being tugged. It was tugged downward so that I was brought to a standstill. The man who tugged it passed me by accompanied by his wife, who chanced to be at my other side, without as much as an excuse-me. It was, in short, a classic example of human rights' infringement but so common is the same act at post offices, churches and bus queues all over the country that it is now regarded as perfectly legal. I was greatly annoyed but, it being the venue that it was, I suffered in silence.

Alas and alack, coat-tugging has been instilled in us

from an early age. It was at its height when public transport was the only means of travel for most people and I have lost count of the number of times my coat was pulled as I was about to board a bus. The coat-puller invariably succeeded in making me forfeit a seat because of my unreadiness for this loathsome form of deception.

Will you tell me which of us has not had his jersey pulled during a football match! It happened to me a hundred times and I am ashamed to say that I was not above pulling gently on the occasional jersey myself especially if the goals of my team were threatened. This, however, rightly or wrongly has to be classified under the heading of self-defence and most referees overlook minor tuggings and pullings that do not really influence the outcome of an encounter. Some referees because of an innate laziness which seems to have become more emphasised lately allow players to pull and drag *ad nauseam*.

Then there is the tail puller who uses the coat of his victim to facilitate ascents. This is quite common and, indeed, expected when the tail puller is intoxicated. Otherwise he might be obliged to remain at the bottom of the incline or whatever until he regained sobriety or until a good Samaritan came along.

If there are tail-pulling ghosts I am certain that they are the ghosts of drunkards rather than footballers. In life footballers have never found it difficult to find their way home after matches whereas the drunkard was nearly always incapable of finding home without assistance.

Then there is the all-too-common coat-tail puller who

is afflicted by shyness and who cannot or will not raise his or her voice for fear of being singled out and that is the bane of all shy folk, being singled out. Hence the propensity towards coat-tail pulling, instead of using the vocal cords.

Then there is the curious party who merely wants to feel the quality of the material of the coat. This happens rarely enough, only when the victim is after purchasing a new coat.

These are but a few of the coat-tail pulling types one is likely to meet in one's travels. Remember if you find it somewhat irksome that it's better than having your leg pulled.

SEVEN SANTAS

MANY OF YOU WILL have heard of the Night of the Long Knives but how many of you have heard of the Night of the Seven Santa Clauses!

Long ago when I was a small boy there was a widespread belief that the original Santa Claus was a fine cut of man which meant that he was tall to begin with. This was one of the reasons why Christmas costumiers made the red coats worn by all Father Christmases so long. As a consequence small men were left in the shade when it came to filling the great annual role.

Personally I believe that Santa Claus was not the broth of a boy he was made out to be. In those days saints were neither large nor fat and it is my guess that he was a middle-sized, hardy sort of chap fit for all weathers.

Anyway let us deal with the Night of the Seven Santa Clauses. It was Christmas Eve and in those days no self-respecting Santa Claus would show himself out of doors until the night before Christmas. The first of the Seven Santa Clauses in question paid his calls from five in the afternoon onwards. The others followed suit at varying times but it so happened that when all the presents had been delivered each and every Santa Claus headed for a certain public house to quench their thirsts and spruce themselves up. One by one they were admitted by the kindly publican, all save the very last one and he was the smallest of the seven. The others were tall and robust and self-assured but the iochtar* of the litter as we shall call him was five feet nothing, spare of frame and would have no bother passing for a flat jockey if he had a mind to.

The trouble started when the kindly publican failed to admit him and the reason the kindly publican did not admit him was because he did not fulfil the requirements for admittance. These were twofold. The first was the requisite knock which consisted of two raps on the door followed by three after a short interval. Alas while the requisite knock was forthcoming the second condition was not fulfilled. This was that the knocker should stand on his toes and show his face at the fanlight above the door. That time, as now, unfortunately there were characters abroad who specialised in creating trouble before and after Christmas. The publican, therefore, had to be sure of the identity of every customer if the peace on his premises was to be maintained. The smallest of the Santa Clauses stood on the very tips of his toes but could not raise his face sufficiently high for identification. He jumped up and down but all to no avail.

Inside the six successful Santa Clauses drank their fill of beer and spirits in view of the season that was in it while the small Santa Claus pined outside. Already he had suffered his share. Because his red coat had been too long he had fallen several times when he stood on the tasselled hem. He still wore the coat proudly even though its length was a great encumbrance. He waited until the next customer came along. It turned out to be a strapping chap who

* *iochtar = runt*

112

knew the knock and had no bother raising himself sufficiently for identification.

'If you don't mind I'll be in with you,' said the small
Santa Claus.

'Indeed you won't,' said the strapping fellow who had
always entertained a secret yearning to play the role of
Santa Claus.

Alas for him there was to be no admission either for
when the kindly publican caught the first glimpse of his
face he resolved that his door should be closed for he recognised the would-be interloper and knew him to be a
chap deficient in both peace and goodwill.

Before he departed from the front of the premises he
drew a clout at the small Santa Claus but while our friend
was too small for the fanlight he was not too small to dis-
patch a blackguard. Drawing his coat tightly around him
he rushed at the midriff of his would-be assailant and flat-
tened him forthwith. When he got to his feet the bully-boy
took off and remained a chastened man for the rest of Christmas. Also thereafter he had a profound respect for small
men which would in time result in a healthy respect for all
men, tall, small and middling, thin, fat and fragile.

The smallest of the Santa Clauses looked at his watch
and saw that the hour of eleven was at hand. Another hour
and it would be midnight and from the looks of things he
would not be allowed to celebrate the arrival of the great
day in the fashion to which he was accustomed.

He headed for home which was an empty home what
with him never having taken a wife or even a lodger to

keep him company. Neither did he keep a cat and the only dog he had ever owned died prematurely in an accident when the creature blindly followed a passing bitch onto the centre of a roadway where a passing bus sent them instantly to that far off land of lamp posts, telephone poles and mahogany kennels.

As he neared home the smallest of the seven Santa Clauses shook his head at the perfidy of it all. Here I am, he told himself, after delivering presents to all and sundry without a drop of whiskey to celebrate Christmas. Here I am, he told himself, full of peace and goodwill with an empty belly as far as drink is concerned. Here I am, he told himself, without a friend in the world and a coat that is too long for me!

With that he slipped and fell to the ground. Manfully he rose but was unable to hold back the tears. When he fell for the second time because of the length of the coat he felt like rising no more. Then he chided himself and reminded himself that no man is ever alone who believes in the real spirit of Christmas and how right he was for down the roadway there came the thunder of twelve pairs of outsized boots and in these boots were the large legs of the other six Santa Clauses who had missed him in the pub and who had yearned for him and who had vowed to find him no matter how far he had strayed.

The largest of all the Santa Clauses lifted him in his arms and raised his great voice aloft.

'There is more joy in heaven,' said he, 'over one sheep who is found than a hundred who are safe and sound.'

'Amen', chorused all the other Santa Clauses. 'Amen', the streets and laneways echoed.

'Amen', said the kindly publican, and all his charges when the missing Santa Claus was restored to his rightful place by the fire and a glass of whiskey placed in his trembling hand.

THE TAKING OF UMBRELLAS

MY UMBRELLA WAS TAKEN last week. I saw it happen but before I could get to my feet and replace my pint glass on the pub counter the umbrella and its new proprietor had disappeared through the front door and presumably round a convenient corner because when I eventually got to the same door the street outside was empty save for a dog half-drowned from the rain. I could be wrong but I thought I saw a smile on the dog's face.

Notice I said that my umbrella was taken, not stolen. I would not regard the unauthorised change of ownership as an act of stealing. Neither would I call it an act of misappropriation. To illegally take a pound of sausages or a loaf of bread is, in my opinion, a far greater offence than stealing an umbrella, especially if the misappropriator is not as hungry as he or she should be. In other words it is all right to steal bread or sausages if one is very hungry but not so when one is not.

The unauthorised taking of umbrellas cannot, of course, be totally condoned but neither can it be condemned for in the taking of umbrellas there are always extenuating circumstances. The man who stole my umbrella was entitled to do so for the good reason that he did not have an umbrella of his own and, in my book, everybody in this world is entitled to an umbrella especially those without caps, hats or any other form of headgear. Having made this clear we may feel free to proceed.

I must concede at this point that there will be readers

who may not look favourably on my somewhat liberal attitude towards umbrella lifting. I personally know several clergymen whose views are diametrically opposed to mine. In the course of their ecclesiastical duties clergymen tend to hand their umbrellas for safe-keeping to whoever happens to be standing next to them. The same applies to bishops but whereas the latter would have a secretary or administrator in attendance your ordinary clergyman would be obliged to depend on a layman.

Laymen, with a few notable exceptions, are a weak-willed, dishonest lot and, more often than not, will not return the clergyman's umbrella. Neither will they pass by an umbrella left behind by chance in a church. The are some who will but these would be the more devout and conscientious types. Normal laymen or Joe Soaps as they are sometimes called look disparagingly on laymen of the aforementioned kind but this is surely because they are incapable of maintaining the high moral codes which are the hallmarks of those they would deride.

The umbrella which was stolen from me was a brolly of inferior quality because I am of the belief that an investment in a quality umbrella is tantamount to lunacy. The better the quality of the umbrella the greater the likelihood that it will be lifted. Nearly all umbrellas which are found on streets or roadways are of inferior quality or tattered or battered or whatever. That's the reason they are left on streets and roadways where they eventually disintegrate. You'll never see a high-class umbrella in a public place unless it has an owner with it.

Let us return to my own umbrella. It was run-of-the-mill but it was serviceable and would just about accommodate the heads and shoulders of two medium-sized adults. The man who took my umbrella was about thirty-five years of age, a pretty tough period in the life of most men, particularly married men because it is the time that bills multiply at an unprecedented rate especially if there are children.

The loss of such a man cannot be reckoned. Apart from the grief which his loss would occasion there is the fact that his family will not have been provided for properly. They never are except in the rarest of cases. They just about manage to make ends meet and rarely invest in luxuries like umbrellas.

I was glad, therefore, that it was my umbrella he took and not the umbrella of some begrudging wretch who cared not whether the poor fellow lived or died. Suppose he had not taken my umbrella and suppose that he incurred a cold followed by pneumonia followed by expiry would not I feel guilty if he had not taken my umbrella!

Why then, the gentle reader will ask, did I follow him to the door! Instinct and nothing more. If I had caught up with him I would not have asked for the return of my umbrella. I would have been annoyed but that's all. Later when my feelings would have cooled I would have been happy to have served my fellow man in some small way.

The gentle reader is sure to ask at this stage if I ever stole an umbrella myself. Of course I did and if I hadn't I wouldn't be alive to tell the tale. I stole an umbrella on a night when torrents of rain deluged the streets and burst the mains. If I hadn't taken the umbrella I would not have survived. But what of the owner of the umbrella! Was he not entitled to some consideration? Of course he was and I'm sure he did the right thing as I did and took another umbrella from the plentiful supply which hung in the hallway of the tavern.

If I might be permitted to parody the late Lord Mac-Aulay I would like to submit the following brief quatrain:

For how can man die better
When facing fearful rain
Than give up his umbrella
And perish earthly gain.
Than give up his umbrella
When every road's a pond
To either a slender, drenched brunette
Or else a dripping blonde.

LET 'EM AT IT

RECENTLY I SPOKE ABOUT do-gooders who intervene in ructions and who often risk life and limb to keep warring factions or individuals apart. They feel they have a duty towards the maintenance of law and order forgetting that other individuals feel they are entitled to savour the mayhem resulting from uninterrupted brawls.

I threw the matter open for discussion in the pub one recent rainy night and I was surprised by the outcome. There was no support whatsoever for the do-gooder. In fact many felt that he should be charged with disorderly conduct for disrupting promising fist fights while others maintained that he should be horsewhipped and drummed out of the community for depriving people of their natural expectations, i.e., watching thuggery, mayhem and what-have-you at no expense to themselves or to the state.

One man admitted that he had assaulted several do-gooders. Apparently he caught them red-handed advising would-be fighters to go home and forget about it. 'I felt like a man,' said he, 'whose television was suddenly turned off just before a big fight or a football game. Here was this disrupter deliberately thwarting the natural drive of angry men, men who only wanted to fight till one or the other dropped.'

He went on to tell me that as soon as he drew a clout at the do-gooder the warring pair turned on him and proceeded to present him with his just desserts. The three made him promise he would never interfere in a fight again.

'There is nothing so frustrating,' said he, 'as preventing a man from inflicting physical damage on another. If these cauldrons of fury are not broached at the right time then it is possible that serious mental damage can be inflicted upon the antagonists, damage that may never heal and which might well result in misdirected retribution in the home upon wives, children and assorted loved ones.' He spoke with considerable conviction and passion. A tear rolled down the side of his face when he recalled the number of times he had been cheated of blood spilling by damnable do-gooders as he called them.

'They should be taken out,' said he, 'and they should be lined up against a wall and shot with frozen gobs of their own blood.'

'Shooting is too good for them,' said another, 'they should be hung, drawn and quartered and cast into the depths of the sea. What right have they to come between two people who hate each other!'

'Ask yourself,' said an elderly gin and tonic, 'who is the most unpopular man in this part of town! Go on. Think now and you'll come up with the right man.'

The name did, in fact, come up and everybody was agreed that he was as unpopular as a Catholic in Windsor Park.

'And why?' asked the man who had posed the question in the first place.

'I'll tell you why my friend. He stopped what would have been the greatest fight of all times by coming between two neighbours with notorious tempers.'

Apparently the neighbours had a falling out over children and squared off from each other preparatory to fighting to a finish. Other neighbours were alerted and soon a sizeable crowd had gathered. Then without warning the do-gooder in question came between the sparring pair and told them to have sense, to think of their wives and families and their good names and so forth and so on. The upshot was that both slunk off into their respective homes and never spoke to each other again. Had they fought to a finish they would surely have made it up afterwards and been friends for life.

A PATHOLOGICAL BUM-PATTER

WE LIVE IN AN age of unpleasant headlines and literary thuggery so I'll refrain from scare tactics and come to the nub of the matter which happens to be the female posterior. I open in this vein because of the reaction I received from one old man who came up to me on the strand at Ballybunion and in a tearful voice confessed that he could be charged with one thousand and eighty-seven counts of posterior patting if the truth were known.

'Where did these offences take place?' I asked.

'Mostly while I was boarding buses,' he explained. Apparently the reason he chose buses was that if the victim turned around the patter could duck or he could bolt or he could stoop to the lowest betrayal of all, i.e., point the finger at an innocent man in the vicinity and then bolt.

This self-confessed posterior patter told me that his conscience was playing on him which surprised me because I never suspected until that very moment that posterior patters had consciences.

'I might not be guilty in the eyes of the law,' he wept, 'but I am guilty in the sight of God.'

He began to weep more copiously so I urged him to walk along the strand with me and answer a few questions so that I could determine the gravity of his patting transgressions.

'I hope and pray,' I told him, 'that those posteriors which you patted were of the mature variety and not those of the underdeveloped, previously unpatted variety.'

'Well,' he said between sobs, 'that's one thing I never did was pat a youthful posterior.'

'And what sort of posteriors did you pat?' I asked him while the waves ran around in front of our feet and threatened to cover our shoes. Overhead the Ballybunion seagulls made a mockery of his confessions while farther out to sea the spume-capped waves formed themselves for a flushing assault on the golden sands where we walked.

He pondered my question for a moment and then he stopped to eye me with a refreshing candour.

'I'll tell you one thing,' he said, 'I never patted a posterior that wasn't patted before.'

'But how could you tell?' I asked him.

Apparently the posteriors he patted were the well-fleshed rumps of middle-aged and even elderly ladies of composed natures and rather cumbersome movements.

'I only patted them that I thought needed it,' he said modestly, 'and to tell you the truth there was very few that took exception. Don't ask me why I do it,' he went on, 'and I won't tell you no lie.'

'And what age are you?' I asked guessing that he was, at the least, a pensioner.

'I'll be eighty in July,' he told me.

'In that case,' I told him, 'you need have no worries because surely the urge to pat will now diminish and die.'

'Oh no sir,' he contradicted, 'the urge to pat is worse than ever it was.'

'And do you confess these things in confession?' I asked trying to sound solemn.

'I does,' he admitted.

'And what does the priest say?'

'He don't seem to take no notice,' came back the ready answer. 'He just gives me my penance and that's the end of it.'

However he went on to tell me that he once told a missioner during a retreat in Listowel in the 1960s that he was a committed posterior patter and there was hell to pay. The missioner lambasted him and told him that he was a fornicator and that if he didn't change his ways he would wind up in hell where the flames would rise blisters on his own posterior day after day, night after night. After that he was fine for awhile but then he chanced to be boarding a bus for Abbeyfeale when what did he see in front of him but a well-rounded posterior. He patted and he knew from the jaded reaction that the proprietress of this enlarged behind was often patted before. She didn't even look around which left him with the impression that his patting style had worsened because of his long lay off. He patted her a second time, this time with more feeling. She turned and she swung her purse which made contact with his jaw. He fell backward stunned and missed the bus. After that he vowed never to pat again but he was up to his old tricks within a week.

'Is there any hope at all for me?' he asked in despair.

'There is,' I told him. 'In fact there is hope for us all. Your best bet is to get a woman of your own and then when you get the desire you can pat away as much as you like and legitimately.'

'No good,' he said, 'I already have a woman of my own but I finds no challenge. There is no risk. I might as well be patting the wall.'

It was plain that there was no more I could do for this poor fellow. His policy seemed to be pat and be damned. Then suddenly he stopped, seemingly to draw his breath. A stout lady was walking against us, a bare twenty paces away. As she passed he extended his left hand behind his back and gave her a fleeting pat on her well-rounded posterior. She leaped a little. She gasped a little. Then she turned round. The inveterate patter of posteriors was gone but not before he tut-tutted reproachfully and pointed an accusing finger in my direction.

'I'm surprised at you,' the woman said and passed on with a scornful toss of her head.

I stood riveted to the ground, betrayed by a pathological bum-patter who cared not a whit for my plight. Overhead the seagulls wheeled and submitted their graceful bodies to the prevailing breezes, their cries taunting me in tones that suggested I should have known better.

CANVASSING

*I wandered lonely as a cloud
That floats on high o'er heath and furze
Till all at once I saw a crowd
A host of olden canvassers.*

I HAVE SEEN GREAT and beautiful sights in my time. Only the other morning while rambling through the bog-lands I beheld a gorse bush bedecked with cobwebs and each cobweb bedecked with raindrops and each raindrop lit by the ascending sun. It was a memorable sight. Only nature can beget such ornamental filigree.

I could mention remote lagoons on the Kerry coast or purple mountains but there is one sight which always restores my belief in humanity and democracy and that is a gallant band of canvassers trudging the highways and byways in search of elusive votes. Armed with nothing more than dreary literature and often poorly protected from the unpredictable elements they pass no door in their quest for ones and twos and threes and even fours and more.

I salute you O courage-filled canvassers of Ireland! Your presence is a guarantee that freedom is assured and that no voter is to be trusted, not even your brother or sister or your mother or even your own wife and that is as it should be for a vote is one's very own and is in permanent hock to nobody.

So it was the other day I encountered my first band of canvassers. They were of the classic variety, seven in number with the candidate in the centre and the area representative in the lead disbursing literature to all who would take it. There was the mandatory wise-cracker or jester who kept everybody in good humour and there were four stalwarts with sober faces and ponderous gait. These were the anchor of the outfit. They never increased their pace not even when it rained.

When I saw them I felt like cheering. They were my assurance that all was well with the world because there are places where canvassers would not dare expose themselves for fear of being maimed or shot or imprisoned. As they neared me they smiled and extended their hands in greeting.

'The oul' number two!' the candidate suggested knowing full well that he did not represent my party.

'Why not!' I said and I meant it. He was the first to ask and he wasn't a bad fellow at all. They moved off about their business and left me to mine.

Seven, I told myself, is sufficient for any group of canvassers. I once canvassed in a group of seventeen and I heard a householder say 'What do they want my vote for if they have all these jokers voting!'

Anything more than seven can be intimidating and in my book the ideal number is five; the candidate or his wife, the jester, the distributor of literature and two able-bodied men as an anchor. The last thing any group wants is a drunken man while on the other hand the odour of freshly-consumed whiskey can be reassuring. It's the stink of stale drink that does the damage. In fact the stink of stale drink will damage any exercise. It does nothing for drink or for the drunkard or for the party.

It is uncivil to ignore canvassers. They have a job to do and if we fail to acknowledge this we fail to acknowledge the electoral system. Not answering the knocks of canvassers is almost as bad as not voting although, come to think of it, there's nothing as bad as not voting. Not voting means giving the nod to the type of government you don't want.

Welcome back then to the canvassers. All they want is a vote, the number one if you can but other preferences will do nicely.

I HAVE DEALT WITH certain aspects of canvassing and may well have overlooked the issuing of pointers and guidelines to aspiring canvassers. I should begin by warning that nobody is more unwelcome at the voters' door than he or she who represents the party responsible for a premature election. A warmer welcome would be guaranteed a process server. The safest bet for such canvassers is to look contrite or even guilty.

All a canvassing party needs apart from seasonal clothing is an armful of literature, a voter's register and a decent looking note-book where the candidate or one of his aides will enter details of complaints, requests and demands from the large variety of householders who may require anything from a new chimney to jobs for out-of-work offspring.

Inexperienced canvassers who will not have been exposed beforehand to pathological liars, i.e., householders who promise every vote in the house to every candidate in every election. So convincing are most of these generous souls that very often an inflated value is placed on the most unlikely candidate. The best way to deal with the pathological liar is to enter into the spirit of the thing so that when he asks the candidate if he can get his son into the garda síochána he should be asked what rank he would like him to start off at. If it happens to be a daughter who wants to get into nursing it should be elicited with the straightest possible face whether she would like to start as a sister or a matron.

The pathological liar who eventually begins to believe his own lies will not be put off by such responses and may well cast a vote in favour of the candidate who has made the most outrageous promises.

There is no penalty suffered by the candidate especially if he is elected because no matter how one blackguards a voter it will not affect the shortness of his memory. Voters are the very opposite of elephants for whereas the elephant never forgets the voter never remembers. There may be some exceptions but these are so few in number that they have little or no effect on the outcome of elections.

I could never admire enough the aplomb of canvassers who have made life-times of promises to the very same householders without ever fulfilling one. There they stand at the door with beaming faces as though they had just presented the sun, the moon and the stars to the unfortunate who comes to answer the door. I know what goes on. I have been a canvasser all too often and have been witness to every make of outrageous promise. I remember once I was taken by surprise when a candidate promised the woman who came to the door that he would get her the old age pension. When she responded that she was only fifty-five he told her she wouldn't have long to wait.

Under no circumstances should canvassing parties be accompanied by dogs, cats, children or gigglers. These take away from solemnity of the group as a whole. Gigglers are the worst because the householder is never sure whether he is the object of the giggles or not. Nobody loves a giggler and a voter is no exception.

To those householders who treat canvassers with indifference I have this to say. Always remember that you are no more than a step away from being a canvasser yourself so that those you have rebuffed may well rebuff you one day. A member of your family may decide to enter politics or if not it may well be an in-law or a neighbour. It may be a fellow-footballer or a former schoolmate or just a friend. Be certain then to welcome all canvassers for any day now it may be your turn to knock upon another man's door.

THERE IS NOTHING AS quirky or deceitful as your common or garden householder when the wrong hand knocks at the door. The right party can bring a beaming face but for the wrong party there is merely a flutter of curtains and a glimpse of a face. This is so that insult might be added to injury. The curtain flutter and the glimpses are deliberate and are really expressions of contempt for the canvassers.

This is better, however, than the female who answers the door immediately, her face writhed in a falsity of smiles, her hands generously extended in welcome. I remember one such creature. When we asked her for her number one she told us with unmistakable sincerity that we would be getting every vote in the house.

One of our party was a lip reader and as we moved away from the house he chanced to turn around. The woman of the smiles was now grinning and hideously grimacing. Our lip-reader informed us that she was referring in the most uncomplimentary terms to our ancestry, to the equally dubious ancestry of the leader of our party and to the illicit sexual extravagance of our mothers and grandmothers.

She also expressed the fond hope, or so our lip reader told us, that we would suffer from excessively loose bowel movements until we eventually expired from these and an assortment of other even more malicious maladies and all this, mark you, from a benign female who had just assured us of every vote in the house.

Yet, for all this, your committed canvasser will go to any lengths to secure votes for his party. He sees the long hours of canvassing and the vicissitudes involved as noble gestures towards the betterment of his country and the betterment of mankind especially those who vote for his party.

Then there are canvassed parties who do not come to the doors of their houses at all. They acknowledge knocks all right but they have no way of knowing who is there for the good reason that they never look out. Faintly from the bowels of the kitchen comes the promise that the canvassers will not be forgotten on polling day, that they were never forgotten and never will be forgotten. It is almost certain that such individuals will not darken the doors of the polling booth on the day of the election. After all if they cannot muster sufficient energy to come to their own doors it is extremely unlikely that they will muster sufficient energy to travel to far-off doors. Then there's the house-holder who merely nods his head silently and closes the door noiselessly after being asked for his vote. He does the same to all canvassers. This man is more than likely to spoil his vote by marking number one in front of every candidate's name.

The biggest blackguard a canvasser is likely to meet in his rounds is the man who insists upon arguing at length about the merits of all the candidates. Beware of this man because he is a prevaricator and as a rule does not have a vote in the area at all. His function is to take up the time of the canvassers. It's his contribution to the war effort for the longer he keeps the canvassers in conversation the less time is at their disposal for the completion of the canvass.

If you were to ask me what was the single most im-portant aspect of canvassing I would have to say that it is making notes, that is to say taking down the gripes and grievances of householders as well as inserting their require-ments for house and road improvements. A good jotter is absolutely necessary and a man with a studious face is priceless for the purpose of making the notes. He must also have an honest appearance and it does not matter a whit whether or not he can write. What matters is that he is seen to be writing. I hope these few tips will be of assistance to the novice canvasser and I would also like to let him know that we are at all times, most of us anyway, mindful of the sacrifices he is making on behalf of his beloved country.

GREAT PUPS

IN THE PUB THE other night the talk turned to greyhounds. Many the hare was coursed and many's the track record was smashed but it was the prospect of mighty things to come that imbued some of our congregation with a feeling of elation. It was not the dogs they had that mattered in the final analysis but rather the dogs to come. One man who spent a half hour boasting about a litter of pups which had recently arrived into the world ran out of steam and headed for the toilet.

After his departure there was a heavy silence upon which a man could lie down and turn over without falling through. It was broken by another greyhound owner, as sage a man as ever slipped a hound.

'That man gone out,' said he, 'had great pups but he never had great dog.'

How true! We place all our hopes in our young whether they are hound, horse or human and we are often disappointed. There was a prodigy in our midst once when I was a boy. In football he could outfield any boy in the school and he could outrun the best. His father once said that he was so fast that he could outrun the wind. The wind must have heard for it didn't blow over two days and two nights. The wind can be like that, unpredictable as ourselves on occasion, blowing hot and cold, blowing gale force and then fanning us gently.

Then another sage in the company wept over the tragic death of a young greyhound who never realised his full potential.

'He was killed,' said his aggrieved owner, 'by a black-guard of a hare that led him up hill and down dale and finally into a quarry hole filled with slime. That hare killed him as sure as Jack and Jill went up the hill.'

Hares were roundly cursed for their cruelty to grey-hounds and one man took off his cap and, weeping into it, brought down a curse on all hares and even rabbits who wouldn't do the decent thing and surrender like they were supposed to do.

Then there was a man amongst us who held forth about one of the greatest pups of all time. 'This pup was so good,' said he, 'that his owner refused £800 for him. This pup was so fast that he passed himself out one day during a long slip and only for he falling over a triopal of rushes he might never have been seen again. I recall no comet his equal. One night he ran up the side of the house after a cat and only for he being frightened of the moon he'd have ruz above the clouds.'

Such a dog! No one spoke for a long spell, a spell that saw a round of drinks consumed and seven heads being scratched.

'What happened him?' a curious listener asked after he had digested the feats of this extraordinary canine.

'They took him to Abbeyfeale and entered him in a trial stake. He got a fair slip but he treated the hare like he'd be his brother and started to chase the other dog.'

'I never heard the like,' said the man who had asked the question.

'He was a homosexual,' explained the man who was telling the story and, apparently a true story, as true as ever was told in connection with greyhounds.

'What did they do with him?' asked the curious listener.

'What they do to all dogs that don't come up to expectations. They bought a pound of sausages and took the dog for a ride as far as the county bounds. The cruel wretches stopped the car and threw out the sausages. There was no need to throw out the dog for he followed the sausages. When he had the sausages ate the car was gone and he was left to wander. Remember that this was the greatest pup of all times so no more about pups this night or I'll go coursing out that door and 'tis me that'll be seen no more.'

FALLS

CHURCH STREET, THE PLACE where I was born in the town of Listowel remains unaffected by time and this is good because the survival of Church Street is important or so I was told the other morning by a resident of that fine thoroughfare.

'Why is the survival of Church Street so important?' I asked him.

He laughed indulgently.

'Because,' said he, 'Church Street is the most northerly street in the town and yet it's no colder than the most southerly.'

This, I had better explain, was a typical Church Street answer.

As we walked down the tall street with its closely-packed, three storeyed houses and friendly faces we decided to have a drink and it was while we were having the drink that we met the stranger. He paid for our drinks and he told us that his father had been a native of Church Street before he emigrated in 1946 to Alberta in Canada.

'I'm disappointed,' he said, 'from my old man's account of the place I expected another Fifth Avenue but all I find is a string of old houses that should be pulled down.'

'Maybe 'tis yourself that wants pulling down.' My friend allowed his anger to get the better of him.

'No offence,' said the Albertan, 'it's just that my old man told me that there wasn't no place in the world like Church Street and all I find is another street with ordinary houses.

I'm not knocking the place,' he went on, 'but I like to call the shots as I see 'em.'

With that he called for two more shots before we had time to reach for our trousers pockets.

When we pointed out that his father remembered Church Street from more than fifty years ago and that his memory would be somewhat prejudiced he heaved a sigh and said, 'I reckon so.'

My friend, a typical Church Streeter went on to provide his own memories of the street for the benefit of the stranger.

'I am an old man now,' he opined, 'but to the day I die I will always remember the sound of the falls at midday.'

'I didn't hear no falls,' the Alberta put in.

'Well I did,' my friend assured him, 'and if you were here when I was a garsún you would have heard them too.'

Personally I was perturbed for I had never heard any falls either after spending nearly half of my life in Church Street. I didn't let on however. I didn't want to let my friend down, this ancient relic of a proud street.

'I remember,' said he, 'when I would be coming from school in the middle of the day I would hear the water falling in torrents and yet there was no rain and there was no piddling.'

'And what the hell did you hear?' asked the Albertan.

'Ah,' said my friend, 'what did I hear but the straining of the spuds for the dinner and the water pouring down from the skillets and the saucepans. In the name of God man sure Niagara Falls was only trotting after it. It didn't last long but while it lasted there was wonderful music as the water hit the shore hole covers. It was often heard in the middle of Bunagara and that's two miles away.'

The Albertan was silenced as my friend continued 'but if you think that the straining of the spuds was something you should be there in the morning when the frying pans opened up. That was the sizzling and the hissing and the flying of hot fat. Remember there were more than two hundred frying pans all operating at the same time, from Cotter's corner up to the library.

> Goodbye to dear old Church Street the place where I was
> born
> How I loved to hear the frying pans when I woke up each
> morn
> The puddings and the sausages, the rashers and the eggs
> Sure you wouldn't hear the likes of it from Cork to Killybegs.'

So sang our friend while I engaged the bar lady's eye. She refilled quickly while my friend endeavoured to teach the lines of the song to the Albertan. Some hours later we decided to go home. We had drunk our fill.

'Look,' said my friend when we went out into the street, 'where would you see it! You talk of moving statues and moving stars but here is a moving street and it wasn't moving at all and we going into the pub. What a street my friends! What a street!'

I LIKE TALKATIVE WOMEN

I KNEW AN ACTOR who always included a few lines of his own whenever he got on the stage. He was a natural talker. It was necessary to tie a piece of fishing gut to his trousers and chuck it hard two or three times to remind him that it was time to give somebody else a chance.

Talking is a God-given gift and an incomparable means of communication. We often hear it said of a woman, that she was a terrible talker. This does not mean that she was a nagger. Yapper would be a more descriptive word.

This woman's husband generally has to wait a long time for his dinner. He doesn't complain, because he knows she can't help it. He knows she is standing at some corner, with her shopping bag in her hand, bemoaning the state of the word with a colleague of the same bent. He knew before he married her that she was an incurable talker and this was one of the reasons why he pursued her. He liked to hear her chattering aimlessly about inconsequential things, and her voice held a music for him that was to be found in no other.

I have heard certain women referred to as talking machines. These can talk for any given length of time, on any subject, from any position you care to name. They can lean out of upstairs windows at unbelievable angles and talk about astronauts – or malt and cod liver oil. They can outline the progress of Ecumenical Councils and debate the outcome of unpredictable football finals. They live for talk, and it is a strange fact that these women are married to men who prefer not to talk at all.

A truly talkative woman will talk under any circumstances. She will talk where it is forbidden to talk, but I believe that no woman should be restrained. I like talkative women. I like to listen to them, and to savour the cadences and pitches of their women's voices. Often, in buses and trains, I have closed my eyes and listened while a woman's voice introduced to me unknown worlds of hats and blouses and shoes and I have convinced myself that there is a lot to be learned from listening, regardless of the subject under discussion.

Sometimes we are not disposed to listen to talk and there is a type who has no regard for the privacy of others. He butts into conversations and contributes opinions where none are wanted. He proceeds, after getting a leg in, to monopolise the conversation and goes on to give nobody else a chance.

There are others, peculiar to rains and buses, who introduce themselves to total strangers, and keep up an irritating flow until the victim is obliged to depart his seat, or tell the intruder to shut up and go away. It is no use pretending to be asleep because the sworn talker is generally contaminated with a voice like a rasp.

I cannot stand loud and obstreperous talkers, or, if you like, aggressive talkers. These are usually to be found in public houses and they generally manage to unsettle the composure of peaceable drinkers so that the pub is no longer a place of retreat. But an old gentleman who owned a country pub was master of occasions like these. He was the possessor of an old gramophone which he turned on whenever a vain-glorious and fight-seeking shouter got out of hand.

There are other quieter types of men who like to talk to themselves. I don't know why some people think it peculiar that other people should talk to themselves. I often talk to myself, sometimes contentedly and other times contentiously. There's many a man who likes to praise himself, and on the other hand, to deride himself, because there is nobody sufficiently interested in him to care whether he deserves praise or blame for his way of living.

Some less endearing types talk to themselves all the time even when they are being addressed by others. There was an old man I knew who talked to himself all the time. He was asked one day by a curious young fellow why he persisted in talking to himself all the while. 'Because I never met a nicer fellow than myself,' the old man replied, 'and I'm also the best listener I know!'

Sometimes, after rows in the home, and outside it, the protagonists do not talk to each other at all for long periods. In the home this is a good thing because it frequently provides a breathing space or lull which is very necessary where people are eternally conscious of each other. Outside the home it is foolish and cruel, and it is always painful to hear of people who do not talk to each other. It is misusing the power of speech and it is a root cause of indigestion and neuralgia.

It passes from one generation to another and, in time, although the breach is not healed, a man forgets his reasons for not talking to another man, so if there's someone to whom you're not talking, put it off no longer. Bid him the time of day the next time you meet, and, as sure as there's meat on the shin of a wren, it won't be long before you'll be talking.